Theme Skills Test
Table of Contents

Practice Test

Read this paragraph. Then read the question. Fill in the circle next to the best answer.

Butterflies and moths are different in several ways. Most moths are active at night. Most butterflies fly during the day. Butterflies have thin, smooth bodies. Most moths have thick, fuzzy bodies. There are knobs on the end of a butterfly's feelers. A moth has fuzzy feelers with no knobs. When a moth lands, it spreads its wings out flat. A butterfly holds its wings together when it is still.

1. What is this paragraph about?
   - ○ **A.** how the bodies of butterflies and moths are shaped
   - ○ **B.** how butterflies and moths hold their wings
   - ○ **C.** how butterflies and moths are different
   - ○ **D.** how some insects fly at night and some fly in the daytime

Off to Adventure!

Level 3, Theme 1

Theme Skills Test Record

Student _____ Date _____

Student Record Form

	Possible Score	Criterion Score	Student Score
Part A: Sequence of Events	5	4	
Part B: Making Inferences	5	4	
Part C: Cause and Effect	5	4	
Part D: Information and Study Skills	5	4	
Part E: Base Words	5	4	
Part F: Syllabication	5	4	
Part G: Inflected Endings	5	4	
Part H: Spelling	10	8	
Part I: Vocabulary	10	8	
Part J: Grammar	10	8	
Part K: Writing Skills	5	4	
TOTAL	70	56	
		Total Student Score x 1.43 =	%

Name _____

Sequence of Events

Read this story. Then read each question. Fill in the circle next to the best answer.

Surprise Adventure

Lee's aunt was taking him on a surprise adventure. Right after breakfast, Lee got out Aunt Terry's list that told him what to bring. First, he found his hiking boots and then his hat. Next, he put a hand shovel and some work gloves into his backpack. Last of all, he made a sandwich and packed a lunch.

Aunt Terry honked the horn, and Lee ran out to the car with his pack. "Are you ready?" asked Aunt Terry.

"I think so," said Lee. "I have everything on the list."

Aunt Terry drove out into the hills. When they arrived at the trailhead they put on their packs. "Are you ready?" asked Aunt Terry. "We're going to hunt for fossils!"

Lee was excited! After hiking for a bit, he found a big rock with something in it. Aunt Terry and Lee dug it out with their shovels. After they cleaned off the rock, Aunt Terry patted Lee on the back. "You found a shell fossil!" she said. "It was probably formed before dinosaurs were even alive."

Lee couldn't believe it. "I've never found a fossil before," he said. "What a great adventure! Thanks, Aunt Terry!"

1. What does Lee do before he gathers the things on the list?
   - ○ **A.** He puts on his hiking boots.
   - ○ **B.** He eats breakfast.
   - ○ **C.** He calls his aunt.
   - ○ **D.** He packs a lunch.

2. Which of these does Lee do first?
   - ○ **F.** He makes a sandwich.
   - ○ **G.** He puts a shovel into his backpack.
   - ○ **H.** He finds his boots and hat.
   - ○ **J.** He waits for his aunt to arrive.

3. When does Lee's aunt tell him they are going to hunt fossils?
   - ○ **A.** after they put on their packs
   - ○ **B.** before breakfast
   - ○ **C.** after they found an interesting rock
   - ○ **D.** before Lee got into the car

4. What happens just before Lee and his aunt clean off the fossil?
   - ○ **F.** Lee thanks his aunt for taking him on the adventure.
   - ○ **G.** They drive to the trailhead.
   - ○ **H.** Lee puts on his pack.
   - ○ **J.** They dig the rock out.

5. Which of these happened first according to the story?
   - ○ **A.** Lee packed the things on Aunt Terry's list.
   - ○ **B.** Aunt Terry drove to the hills.
   - ○ **C.** Lee found the shell fossil.
   - ○ **D.** Lee packed his lunch.

Name _____

Making Inferences

Read this story. Then read each question. Fill in the circle next to the best answer.

The Surprise in the Old Barn

Ronny and his brother, Tyrone, arrived at Grandpa Jack's farm. As soon as they got there, they raced to the old barn. They couldn't wait to go exploring. At home they usually played at the park or took a bus to the mall. But they loved visiting Grandpa Jack and his farm because there were many different things to do.

"Let's see what's up in the loft," said Ronny. He climbed up the ladder, and Tyrone followed him. In the corner of the loft, they found an old trunk covered in dust.

Tyrone brushed the dust off and opened the lid. "Wow, there's a lot of old stuff in here. Look at this old rope," he said.

"And here's an old rodeo poster," said Ronny. "Hey! One of the cowboy names on it is Slim Simmons. Simmons is our last name!"

Tyrone found an old statue of a cowboy on a horse. It had the words *Grand Prize, Roping* on it. "Look at this," he said, holding it up. Tyrone thought for a moment. "Do you think that Grandpa Jack...?"

"I don't know," said Ronny before Tyrone could finish his question. "Let's go talk to Grandpa Jack right now!"

"Don't you mean Grandpa Slim?" asked Tyrone as he ran to catch up with his brother.

1. What helps you infer that the boys are excited about visiting Grandpa Jack's farm?
   - ○ **A.** They had just arrived at the farm.
   - ○ **B.** They couldn't wait to go exploring.
   - ○ **C.** They play in the park when they are at home.
   - ○ **D.** They climb the ladder in the barn.

2. How do you think the boys feel when they find the items in the trunk?
   - ○ **F.** They are surprised.
   - ○ **G.** They feel sad.
   - ○ **H.** They are scared.
   - ○ **J.** They feel worried.

3. What do the boys' actions tell you about them?
   - ○ **A.** They are unfair.
   - ○ **B.** They are rude.
   - ○ **C.** They are curious.
   - ○ **D.** They are foolish.

4. Why do you think the boys' grandfather put the items in a trunk?
   - ○ **F.** He didn't have enough room in the trash.
   - ○ **G.** He moved homes and forgot to unpack them.
   - ○ **H.** There is no room in his farmhouse.
   - ○ **J.** He wants to keep them safe.

5. What do you think the boys will ask their grandfather about?
   - ○ **A.** what being a famous cowboy was like
   - ○ **B.** what the name of his horse was
   - ○ **C.** how the trunk got into the barn
   - ○ **D.** how he met their grandmother

STOP

Name _____

Cause and Effect

Read this story. Then read each question. Fill in the circle next to the best answer.

A Hike in Bear Country

Frank's scout troop was getting set to go hiking in Montana. Frank loved camping and was excited about the trip. He went to the library and got several books about hiking in Montana. The more he read, the more worried he became. He learned that there were many bears in the mountains where they would be hiking.

On the bus ride to Montana, Frank didn't enjoy the trip because he was so worried about bears. He hardly noticed the beautiful scenery. He didn't join in the songs his friends sang and hardly ate his lunch.

The morning that the troop started up the trail, Mr. Scott, the scout master, talked to the boys about bears. "Since bears want to stay away from people, they'll leave if they hear us coming," he said. He tied some bells to each boy's walking stick. "These will give the bears plenty of warning. We'll be safe if we stay together and stay on the trail."

The bells made Frank feel a bit safer. He started enjoying the hike and being with his friends. By the end of the day, Frank was relaxed and happy. As they headed back down to camp, he thought to himself, "Bear country hiking isn't so bad!"

1. What causes Frank to begin worrying about bears?
   - ○ **A.** something that his scout master said
   - ○ **B.** information in books that he read
   - ○ **C.** stories that his friends told about bears
   - ○ **D.** a newspaper report about a bear attack

2. Why doesn't Frank sing songs or enjoy the scenery while on the bus?
   - ○ **F.** He is carsick.
   - ○ **G.** He sleeps during the drive.
   - ○ **H.** He is angry at his friends.
   - ○ **J.** He is worried about bears.

3. What effect do the bells have on the bears?
   - ○ **A.** They make bears too sleepy to attack.
   - ○ **B.** Bears have sensitive ears and can't stand noise.
   - ○ **C.** They give bears warning that someone is approaching.
   - ○ **D.** Bells let bears know that people are coming so the bears can attack them.

4. What effect do the bells have on Frank?
   - ○ **F.** He feels safe.
   - ○ **G.** He becomes nervous.
   - ○ **H.** He wakes up.
   - ○ **J.** He feels scared.

5. What happens when Frank starts enjoying the hike and his friends?
   - ○ **A.** He says that he loves hiking.
   - ○ **B.** He becomes hungry.
   - ○ **C.** He starts singing.
   - ○ **D.** He relaxes and feels happy.

STOP

 Name _____

Information and Study Skills

Read each question. Then fill in the circle next to the best answer.

1. On which page of a book would you find the name of its author?
    ○ **A.** title page   ○ **C.** glossary
    ○ **B.** table of contents ○ **D.** index

2. In which part of a book would you find a list of words and their meanings?
    ○ **F.** title page   ○ **H.** glossary
    ○ **G.** table of contents ○ **J.** index

3. Which of these chapter titles would give you information about steering a boat?
    ○ **A.** Chapter 1: Sailing
    ○ **B.** Chapter 2: Parachuting
    ○ **C.** Chapter 3: Rock Climbing
    ○ **D.** Chapter 4: Scuba Diving

4. Which part of a book lists all the subjects covered and the pages on which they are found?
    ○ **F.** title page   ○ **H.** glossary
    ○ **G.** table of contents ○ **J.** index

5. Where would you look in a book to find out if there is a chapter on rock climbing?
    ○ **A.** title page
    ○ **B.** table of contents
    ○ **C.** glossary
    ○ **D.** index

STOP

E Name _____

Base Words

Read each sentence. Choose the base word for the underlined word. Then fill in the circle next to the base word.

1. The family was <u>hiking</u> on the trail at sunrise.
   - ○ **A.** hiker
   - ○ **B.** hiked
   - ○ **C.** hikes
   - ○ **D.** hike

2. They <u>prepared</u> breakfast over the campfire.
   - ○ **F.** prep
   - ○ **G.** prepar
   - ○ **H.** prepare
   - ○ **J.** preparing

3. The son picked up leaves for his leaf <u>collection</u>.
   - ○ **A.** collecting
   - ○ **B.** collec
   - ○ **C.** collect
   - ○ **D.** coll

4. The father and the daughter saw a beaver <u>hurrying</u> into the woods.
   - ○ **F.** hurry
   - ○ **G.** hurries
   - ○ **H.** hurr
   - ○ **J.** hurried

5. Their <u>friendly</u> dog barked and wagged its tail.
   - ○ **A.** friends
   - ○ **B.** friend
   - ○ **C.** frien
   - ○ **D.** friendliness

Syllabication

Read each sentence. Then choose the best way to divide each underlined word into syllables. Fill in the circle next to the best answer.

1. Sandra learned to <u>snorkel</u> on her vacation.
   - ○ **A.** snor • kel
   - ○ **B.** sno • rkel
   - ○ **C.** snorke • l
   - ○ **D.** sn • orkel

2. Sandra and her <u>sister</u> Jean snorkeled along the coral reef.
   - ○ **F.** siste • r
   - ○ **G.** si • ster
   - ○ **H.** sist • er
   - ○ **J.** sis • ter

3. Jean pointed to a <u>stingray</u> half buried in the sand.
   - ○ **A.** sting • ray
   - ○ **B.** sti • ngray
   - ○ **C.** stin • gray
   - ○ **D.** st • ingray

4. The girls saw <u>bubbles</u> coming from a scuba diver below them.
   - ○ **F.** bubb • les
   - ○ **G.** bu • bbles
   - ○ **H.** bub • bles
   - ○ **J.** bubbl • es

5. Sandra saw a beautiful angelfish <u>swimming</u> near the coral.
   - ○ **A.** swi • mming
   - ○ **B.** swim • ming
   - ○ **C.** sw • imming
   - ○ **D.** swimm • ing

G Name _____

Inflected Endings

Read each sentence. Choose the base word and ending for each underlined word. Fill in the circle next to the best answer.

1. Sharon was <u>preparing</u> for her trip.
   - ○ **A.** pre + paring
   - ○ **B.** prepare + ing
   - ○ **C.** prepar + ing
   - ○ **D.** prep + aring

2. She would be <u>assisting</u> doctors in a tiny village.
   - ○ **F.** assis + ting
   - ○ **G.** assi + sting
   - ○ **H.** assist + ing
   - ○ **J.** assisti + ng

3. Her mother <u>gathered</u> some final things for the trip.
   - ○ **A.** gath + ered
   - ○ **B.** gathe + red
   - ○ **C.** ga + thered
   - ○ **D.** gather + ed

4. Her father <u>snapped</u> pictures at the airport.
   - ○ **F.** snap + ed
   - ○ **G.** snap + ped
   - ○ **H.** sna + pped
   - ○ **J.** snapp + ed

5. Sharon's heart was <u>pounding</u> as she got on the plane.
   - ○ **A.** poun + ding
   - ○ **B.** poun + ing
   - ○ **C.** pound + ing
   - ○ **D.** pound + ng

STOP

Spelling

Read each sentence. Find the correctly spelled word to complete each sentence. Fill in the circle next to your answer.

1. Mei had an adventure at the museum _____ week.
   - ○ **A.** lastt
   - ○ **B.** lasst
   - ○ **C.** last
   - ○ **D.** laste

2. She was _____ behind when her class got on the bus to return to school.
   - ○ **F.** left
   - ○ **G.** lefft
   - ○ **H.** leeft
   - ○ **J.** lefte

3. Mei looked around and saw a _____ of people, but no one from her class.
   - ○ **A.** laht
   - ○ **B.** laut
   - ○ **C.** lote
   - ○ **D.** lot

4. Her bad _____ got worse when the museum elevator stopped between floors.
   - ○ **F.** luck
   - ○ **G.** luk
   - ○ **H.** lucke
   - ○ **J.** luc

5. A guard saw that the elevator had stopped and came to _____ Mei.
   - ○ **A.** savv
   - ○ **B.** save
   - ○ **C.** saev
   - ○ **D.** sav

Go on

6. Mei breathed a _____ sigh when she saw the guard.
- ○ **F.** hyuge
- ○ **G.** hoog
- ○ **H.** hugge
- ○ **J.** huge

7. She and the guard looked where the buses were parked, but a _____ fog made it hard to see.
- ○ **A.** thikk
- ○ **B.** thicke
- ○ **C.** thick
- ○ **D.** thik

8. Mei saw her teacher rushing toward her with a big _____.
- ○ **F.** smile
- ○ **G.** smiel
- ○ **H.** smill
- ○ **J.** smyle

9. Her teacher said she had never been so worried in her _____!
- ○ **A.** lyef
- ○ **B.** liff
- ○ **C.** life
- ○ **D.** lyfe

10. That night, Mei wrote a thank-you _____ to the guard.
- ○ **F.** noht
- ○ **G.** note
- ○ **H.** nott
- ○ **J.** nohte

Name _____

Vocabulary

Study the dictionary entry below. Use the entry to find the answer to Questions 1 through 7. Fill in the circle next to the best answer.

> **litter** _noun_ **1.** Paper, cans, and other trash left on the ground.
> **2.** A group of animals born to one mother at the same time.
> **3.** The board a wounded or sick person is carried on. ◆ _verb_
> **1.** To leave trash lying about: _Please don't litter the campsite._
> **2.** To scatter around: _Clothes and toys littered his room._
> **lit•ter** (lĭt′ ər) ◆_noun, plural_ **litters** ◆ _verb_ **littered, littering**

1. What **two** parts of speech is _litter_?
   - ○ **A.** noun and adjective
   - ○ **B.** noun and verb
   - ○ **C.** verb and plural
   - ○ **D.** verb and adverb

2. Which of the following is the **second most common** definition of _litter_ as a noun?
   - ○ **F.** the board a wounded or sick person is carried on
   - ○ **G.** to scatter around
   - ○ **H.** paper, cans, and other trash left on the ground
   - ○ **J.** a group of animals born to one mother at the same time

Go on

3. What part of the dictionary entry is (lĭt′ ər)?

- ○ **A.** the first meaning
- ○ **B.** the pronunciation
- ○ **C.** the part of speech
- ○ **D.** the entry word

4. Where in the entry are the other forms of the word *litter* shown?

- ○ **F.** in the middle of the entry
- ○ **G.** at the beginning of the entry
- ○ **H.** at the end of the entry
- ○ **J.** before the entry

5. Which meaning matches the use of *litter* in this sentence?

My father didn't like it when I littered my room with camping gear.

- ○ **A.** to scatter around
- ○ **B.** to leave trash lying about
- ○ **C.** paper, cans, and other trash left on the ground
- ○ **D.** a group of animals born to one mother at the same time

6. Which meaning matches the use of *litter* in this sentence?

Before we left the campground, our troop picked up all of our litter.

- ○ **F.** to scatter around
- ○ **G.** paper, cans, and other trash left on the ground
- ○ **H.** a group of animals born to one mother at the same time
- ○ **J.** to leave trash lying about

7. Which meaning matches the use of *litter* in this sentence?

Thankfully, none of us had to be carried out of the mountains on a litter.

- ○ **A.** a group of animals born to one mother at the same time
- ○ **B.** to leave trash lying about
- ○ **C.** paper, cans, and other trash left on the ground
- ○ **D.** the board a wounded or sick person is carried on

Go on ⇨

Read each group of words. Fill in the circle next to the word that would come first in a dictionary.

8. ○ **F.** mountain
   ○ **G.** motorcycle
   ○ **H.** month
   ○ **J.** moonlight

9. ○ **A.** hike
   ○ **B.** high
   ○ **C.** hiss
   ○ **D.** hill

10. ○ **F.** adventure
    ○ **G.** admit
    ○ **H.** addition
    ○ **J.** adult

Name _____

Grammar

Read each question. Fill in the circle next to the best answer.

1. Which of these is a sentence?
   - ○ **A.** Sandra and her family.
   - ○ **B.** They are planning a bicycle tour.
   - ○ **C.** Riding for four days.
   - ○ **D.** Camping out along the way.

2. Which of these is **not** a sentence?
   - ○ **F.** Marty has a new bike.
   - ○ **G.** His parents helped him choose it.
   - ○ **H.** Learning the safety rules.
   - ○ **J.** He always wears a helmet.

3. Which of these is a command?
   - ○ **A.** Is that a bicycle for two?
   - ○ **B.** The back seat is small enough for a child.
   - ○ **C.** Get on and try it.
   - ○ **D.** I've never had so much fun!

4. Which of these is a question?
   - ○ **F.** What a loud pop that was!
   - ○ **G.** Help me fix this flat tire.
   - ○ **H.** The new tube is in my backpack.
   - ○ **J.** Do you know how to pump up the tire?

5. Which of these is an exclamation?

- ○ **A.** We're planning a neighborhood bicycle race.
- ○ **B.** What a great idea that is!
- ○ **C.** Will the race include children and adults?
- ○ **D.** Invite your whole family to come.

6. Which of these is a statement?

- ○ **F.** What will happen after the race?
- ○ **G.** There will be a big cookout.
- ○ **H.** It will be lots of fun!
- ○ **J.** Come and have burgers and pie with us.

7. What is the subject of this sentence?

All the riders put their packs in the van.

- ○ **A.** All
- ○ **B.** put their packs
- ○ **C.** All the riders
- ○ **D.** packs in the van

8. What is the predicate of this sentence?

The group rode the first ten miles in one hour.

- ○ **F.** rode the first ten miles in one hour
- ○ **G.** The group
- ○ **H.** the first ten miles
- ○ **J.** in one hour

9. What is the predicate of this sentence?

The first riders arrived at the campsite at four o'clock.

- ○ **A.** at the campsite at four o'clock
- ○ **B.** at the campsite
- ○ **C.** The first riders
- ○ **D.** arrived at the campsite at four o'clock

10. What is the subject of this sentence?

Everyone enjoyed a big meal after the long ride.

- ○ **F.** after the long ride
- ○ **G.** Everyone
- ○ **H.** enjoyed a big meal
- ○ **J.** a big meal

Name _____

Writing Skills

Read each sentence. Choose the sentence that shows the correct way to use commas. Fill in the circle next to the best answer.

1. ○ **A.** Our plane landed in Durango Colorado.
   ○ **B.** Our plane landed in, Durango Colorado.
   ○ **C.** Our plane landed in Durango, Colorado.
   ○ **D.** Our plane landed, in Durango Colorado.

2. ○ **F.** We had tickets to ride the narrow gauge train on May 24 2001.
   ○ **G.** We had tickets to ride the narrow gauge train on, May 24 2001.
   ○ **H.** We had tickets to ride the narrow gauge train on May 24, 2001.
   ○ **J.** We had tickets to ride the narrow gauge train on May, 24, 2001.

3. ○ **A.** The train took us to Silverton Colorado and back.
   ○ **B.** The train took us to Silverton, Colorado, and back.
   ○ **C.** The train took us to Silverton, Colorado and back.
   ○ **D.** The train took us to, Silverton Colorado, and back.

Read each group of sentences. Choose the sentence that shows the correct way to write days of the week. Fill in the circle next to the best answer.

4. ○ **F.** The train museum was closed on sunday and monday.
○ **G.** The train museum was closed on Sunday and monday.
○ **H.** The train museum was closed on sunday and Monday.
○ **J.** The train museum was closed on Sunday and Monday.

5. ○ **A.** On Tuesday the engineer told us that the biggest crowds rode the train on Saturdays.
○ **B.** On Tuesday the engineer told us that the biggest crowds rode the train on saturdays.
○ **C.** On tuesday the engineer told us that the biggest crowds rode the train on saturdays.
○ **D.** On tuesday the engineer told us that the biggest crowds rode the train on Saturdays.

Celebrating Traditions

Level 3, Theme 2

Theme Skills Test Record

Student _____ Date _____

Student Record Form

	Possible Score	Criterion Score	Student Score
Part A: Author's Viewpoint	5	4	
Part B: Categorize and Classify	5	4	
Part C: Noting Details	5	4	
Part D: Topic, Main Idea, and Supporting Details	5	4	
Part E: Information and Study Skills	5	4	
Part F: Compound Words	5	4	
Part G: Plural Endings	5	4	
Part H: Contractions	5	4	
Part I: Plural Endings	5	4	
Part J: Spelling	10	8	
Part K: Vocabulary	10	8	
Part L: Grammar	10	8	
Part M: Writing Skills	5	4	
TOTAL	80	64	
	Total Student Score x 1.25 =		%

Author's Viewpoint

Read this story. Then read each question. Fill in the circle next to the best answer.

Memorial Day

Memorial Day is a day for remembering. We honor the soldiers who died for our country. In my town, the day is filled with traditions. The most important thing we do is decorating graves at the local cemetery. We put flags and flowers on the soldiers' graves. Then the mayor gives a speech. He talks about what the soldiers did for the country. It makes us think about how we can help our country.

Next, there is a parade down Main Street. Soldiers march in front. Boy Scouts and Girl Scouts carry banners. Next come the people who fought in wars. Some walk, and some ride in wheelchairs. Everyone cheers for them. As the flag passes, people, including the children, put their hands on their hearts. We think about the brave soldiers who died.

Then we have a town picnic. At the picnic, we listen to an inspiring speech. It is the famous Gettysburg Address. Abraham Lincoln gave the speech to honor soldiers who died in the Civil War. After the speech, we sing our favorite songs about America.

The day helps everyone remember the past. It makes us grateful to the people who fought for our country.

1. What does the author think is the most important Memorial Day tradition?
   - ○ **A.** watching the parade
   - ○ **B.** listening to the Gettysburg Address
   - ○ **C.** going to the Memorial Day picnic
   - ○ **D.** decorating the soldiers' graves

2. How does the author feel toward people who died for their country?
   - ○ **F.** sad
   - ○ **G.** upset
   - ○ **H.** grateful
   - ○ **J.** disappointed

3. Why does the author leave out details about children running and playing at the picnic?
   - ○ **A.** She wants to show that the holiday has a serious meaning.
   - ○ **B.** Children are not important.
   - ○ **C.** No children were there.
   - ○ **D.** She doesn't like children.

4. Which word describes how the author feels about the Gettysburg Address?
   - ○ **F.** entertained
   - ○ **G.** bored
   - ○ **H.** inspired
   - ○ **J.** tired

5. Which statement best represents the author's overall message?
   - ○ **A.** We should all help keep cemeteries clean.
   - ○ **B.** We should remember those who died for their country.
   - ○ **C.** Picnics are good because they help bring people together.
   - ○ **D.** Everyone should go to a parade.

STOP

Categorize and Classify

Read this story. Then read each question. Fill in the circle next to the best answer.

Our New Year's Celebration

I love New Year's Eve. We have a big party at my grandparents' house in the country. My aunts and uncles drive in from all around the state. My parents leave work early so we can have enough time to get there in the snow. We usually arrive first. When we do, my brother and I go sledding and then wait by the fire for our cousins to show up.

Everyone brings something for the party. Grandma bakes bread. Uncle Jerry always cooks a ham. Aunt Sarah makes a pot of black-eyed peas. My cousin Buck has a sweet tooth, so he brings brownies for everyone.

Before supper, I have fun with my cousins. Some of the older cousins play cards. Some throw snowballs at each other. The younger children play chase or hide-and-seek. Others play football in the snow.

After we eat supper, everyone bundles up and sits on the front porch. At midnight, fireworks explode in the sky. We blow horns and bang on pans. It's fun to make so much noise!

The next day everyone packs up and goes home. We will see each other again on the Fourth of July and Thanksgiving. We always have a good time, but New Year's Eve is still my favorite family celebration.

Go on

1. Which of the following would describe all the people mentioned in the first paragraph?
   - ○ **A.** relatives
   - ○ **B.** neighbors
   - ○ **C.** people
   - ○ **D.** children

2. Which of the following foods would you classify under Dessert?
   - ○ **F.** bread
   - ○ **G.** ham
   - ○ **H.** black-eyed peas
   - ○ **J.** brownies

3. What category includes all of the things the cousins do before supper?
   - ○ **A.** Contests
   - ○ **B.** Jokes
   - ○ **C.** Games
   - ○ **D.** Sports

4. Which of these belongs in the category My Family's New Year's Eve Traditions?
   - ○ **F.** sleeping outside
   - ○ **G.** going to sleep early
   - ○ **H.** playing only indoor games
   - ○ **J.** watching fireworks

5. Which category includes Fourth of July, Thanksgiving, and New Year's Eve?
   - ○ **A.** Days of the Week
   - ○ **B.** Holidays
   - ○ **C.** Games
   - ○ **D.** Vacations

STOP

Name _____

Noting Details

Read this story. Then read each question. Fill in the circle next to the best answer.

Kristen Learns a Family Recipe

"Mom, it's snowing too hard to play outside," complained Kristen.

"Well, then," her mother said. "This is a great afternoon to share a family tradition. I'll teach you how to make the cookies that your great-great-grandmother used to make."

Kristen was curious. "How do you know the recipe?"

"Your great-great-grandmother shared the recipe with her daughter. That was my grandmother. And she taught my mother the recipe." Kristen's mother looked at a picture of her own mother and smiled. "I still remember the smell of those wonderful cookies baking the day that Mom taught me this recipe."

Kristen couldn't wait to make the cookies. She helped her mother make the dough. They mixed butter, sugar, eggs, milk, lemon juice, and flour. While the dough chilled, Kristen and her mother made the filling. They boiled raisins in water and added sugar and vanilla. Kristen cut out circles of dough. She put a little raisin filling in each one.

When the cookies were done baking, they were soft and lemony. Best of all, there were sweet raisins in the middle.

"What other family recipes do you know?" asked Kristen. "I want to start a family recipe book!"

Go on

1. In what season does the story probably take place?
   - ○ **A.** winter
   - ○ **B.** spring
   - ○ **C.** summer
   - ○ **D.** fall

2. What does Kristen's mother remember best about the day she learned to make the cookies?
   - ○ **F.** the sweet taste of the cookies
   - ○ **G.** the weather
   - ○ **H.** stirring the dough
   - ○ **J.** the smell of the cookies

3. How do you know that the recipe makes Kristen's mother remember her own mother?
   - ○ **A.** She tells Kristen it is a great afternoon.
   - ○ **B.** She helps Kristen make the dough.
   - ○ **C.** She looks at her mother's picture and smiles.
   - ○ **D.** She helps Kristen gather the ingredients.

4. Which is an ingredient that Kristen uses to make the dough?
   - ○ **F.** lemon juice
   - ○ **G.** raisins
   - ○ **H.** filling
   - ○ **J.** vanilla

5. What detail shows you that family is important to Kristen?
   - ○ **A.** She stays inside to bake.
   - ○ **B.** She looks at her grandmother's picture.
   - ○ **C.** She wants to make a book of family recipes.
   - ○ **D.** She helps her mother make the dough.

Topic, Main Idea, and Supporting Details

Read this passage. Then read each question. Fill in the circle next to the best answer.

Fun in the Sun

Every summer, my family packs up and heads for Sunnyside Beach. The fun begins as soon as we are on the road. During the trip, we talk and sing songs. We stop for a picnic at our favorite roadside park. As we get closer to the beach, we point out familiar sights.

We always stay in the same beach house. It has big, sunny rooms and a porch with a swing. My dad loves to read in the hammock out back. The owner, Mrs. Pitts, always leaves a plate of homemade cookies on the kitchen table.

Of course, the best part of our vacation is swimming in the ocean and playing on the beach. Every morning, we go for a long swim. We draw pictures in the wet sand and make sand sculptures. In the afternoons, we take walks along the beach. We collect shells and smooth rocks.

When our vacation is over, we pack up the pretty things we've found. It's hard to leave, but we know we'll be back again next summer.

1. What is the topic of this passage?
   - ○ **A.** a summertime tradition
   - ○ **B.** ways to have fun with your family
   - ○ **C.** things to do while driving with your family
   - ○ **D.** learning to love nature

2. What is the main idea of the first paragraph?
   - ○ **F.** The family drives to the same beach every summer.
   - ○ **G.** They like the beach house where they always stay.
   - ○ **H.** They stop for a picnic.
   - ○ **J.** The drive to the beach is fun.

3. Which detail best supports the main idea of the first paragraph?
   - ○ **A.** The owner bakes cookies for the family.
   - ○ **B.** They talk and sing as they drive.
   - ○ **C.** The name of the beach is Sunnyside Beach.
   - ○ **D.** They pack the car.

4. What is the main idea of the third paragraph?
   - ○ **F.** Playing on the beach and swimming in the ocean are fun.
   - ○ **G.** There are shells on the beach.
   - ○ **H.** Walking is good for you.
   - ○ **J.** Morning is the best time for a long swim.

5. Which detail supports the main idea of the third paragraph?
   - ○ **A.** The family always stays at the same house.
   - ○ **B.** The family eats at their favorite roadside park.
   - ○ **C.** The family draws pictures in the sand.
   - ○ **D.** The father reads in the hammock.

Information and Study Skills

Read this passage. Then read each question. Fill in the circle next to the best answer.

The Quilting Tradition

The tradition of quilting began many years ago. Cloth was expensive, so people would try and find many uses for it. For example, when clothes would wear out, people would cut them up into scraps of different shapes and sizes. These pieces would then be arranged into pretty patterns and sewn together.

It took lots of time and work to make a quilt. When one woman pieced her scraps together into a pattern, she would bring it to a quilting bee. At a quilting bee, many friends would sit around a large wooden frame and help finish the quilt. They would laugh and tell stories as they worked.

People still enjoy making quilts today. First, a design is chosen for the quilt. Next, cloth pieces are cut and sewn together. This forms the quilt top. When the top is ready, a piece of cloth that is a little larger than the top is laid out. This is the backing for the quilt. A sheet of stuffing, or batting, is spread on top of this. Next, with the finished side facing up, the quilt top is placed on the batting. The three layers are then stretched out smoothly on a frame. Finally, the layers are stitched together to form the finished quilt.

1. If you were taking notes, what would be the best main heading
    for the topic of the passage?
    - ○ **A.** Quilts of Today
    - ○ **B.** Putting a Quilt Together
    - ○ **C.** Uses for Cloth
    - ○ **D.** Kinds of Quilts

2. Which of these details about the topic is most important?
    - ○ **F.** Quilts are made out of cloth.
    - ○ **G.** People enjoy making quilts.
    - ○ **H.** Batting is the stuffing inside a quilt.
    - ○ **J.** Quilting is an old tradition that is still enjoyed today.

3. Which of these details about the topic is least important?
    - ○ **A.** Today, the first thing quilters do is choose a design.
    - ○ **B.** The cloth pieces are arranged into a pretty pattern.
    - ○ **C.** Clothes wear out.
    - ○ **D.** Cloth was expensive so it was reused to make quilts.

4. What key word or words could you use that best fit the
    information in the second paragraph?
    - ○ **F.** Quilting Bees
    - ○ **G.** Patterns
    - ○ **H.** Cloth
    - ○ **J.** Design

5. Which question could you ask that best fits the information in the
    last paragraph?
    - ○ **A.** Why are quilts still made today?
    - ○ **B.** How is a quilt put together these days?
    - ○ **C.** What is a quilting bee?
    - ○ **D.** What is batting?

STOP

Name _____

Compound Words

Read each sentence. Find the compound word and fill in the circle next to your answer.

1. My family celebrated my birthday with all of our usual traditions.
   - ○ **A.** family
   - ○ **B.** birthday
   - ○ **C.** celebrated
   - ○ **D.** traditions

2. In the morning, my entire family came to my bedroom with balloons and sang to me.
   - ○ **F.** morning
   - ○ **G.** entire
   - ○ **H.** bedroom
   - ○ **J.** balloons

3. In the afternoon, we had a picnic at the park and broke a piñata.
   - ○ **A.** afternoon
   - ○ **B.** picnic
   - ○ **C.** broke
   - ○ **D.** piñata

4. Everyone gave me presents and laughed and clapped as I opened them.
   - ○ **F.** Everyone
   - ○ **G.** presents
   - ○ **H.** laughed
   - ○ **J.** opened

5. The party didn't end until after sunset.
   - ○ **A.** party
   - ○ **B.** didn't
   - ○ **C.** until
   - ○ **D.** sunset

Plural Endings

Read each sentence. Choose the correct base word and ending for each underlined word. Fill in the circle next to the best answer.

1. Our neighborhood has block <u>parties</u> all summer long.
   ○ **A.** party + s   ○ **C.** parti + es
   ○ **B.** party + es   ○ **D.** party + ies

2. We close off the streets and put out picnic <u>tables</u> for the food.
   ○ **F.** table + es   ○ **H.** table + s
   ○ **G.** tables + s   ○ **J.** tabl + es

3. All of the <u>families</u> bring good food to share.
   ○ **A.** family + es   ○ **C.** family + ies
   ○ **B.** family + s   ○ **D.** famili + es

4. Some of the neighbors like to give <u>speeches</u> about how much they enjoy the neighborhood.
   ○ **F.** speech + s   ○ **H.** speeche + s
   ○ **G.** speech + es   ○ **J.** spee + ches

5. When the fun is over, we use paper <u>towels</u> to clean up.
   ○ **A.** tow + les   ○ **C.** tow + els
   ○ **B.** towel + es   ○ **D.** towel + s

STOP

Name _____

Contractions

Read each sentence. Choose the word or words that stand for the underlined word. Fill in the circle next to the best answer.

1. <u>We're</u> planning a Fourth of July parade for our neighborhood.
    - ○ **A.** We was
    - ○ **B.** Were
    - ○ **C.** We are
    - ○ **D.** We would

2. Steve says <u>he's</u> planning to paint his bike red, white, and blue.
    - ○ **F.** he did
    - ○ **G.** he would
    - ○ **H.** he will
    - ○ **J.** he is

3. Lily will be on vacation so she <u>won't</u> be able to come.
    - ○ **A.** won not
    - ○ **B.** will not
    - ○ **C.** were not
    - ○ **D.** was not

4. Pat and Sonya say that <u>they'll</u> pass out flags to everyone who comes.
    - ○ **F.** there will
    - ○ **G.** they would
    - ○ **H.** they will
    - ○ **J.** they were

5. Some people say <u>they're</u> going to walk their pets in the parade.
    - ○ **A.** they are
    - ○ **B.** their
    - ○ **C.** there
    - ○ **D.** they will

Name _____

Plural Endings

Read each sentence. Then choose the correct plural form of the word in ( ) to complete each sentence. Fill in the circle next to your answer.

1. The third-grade _____ are putting on a Thanksgiving program. (class)
   - ○ **A.** clases
   - ○ **B.** classies
   - ○ **C.** classes
   - ○ **D.** classess

2. Mrs. Downing brought in four large _____ of costumes. (box)
   - ○ **F.** boxes
   - ○ **G.** boxs
   - ○ **H.** boxxes
   - ○ **J.** boxies

3. The girls will be wearing old-fashioned Pilgrim _____. (dress)
   - ○ **A.** dreses
   - ○ **B.** dresses
   - ○ **C.** dressses
   - ○ **D.** dress

4. We put picnic tables and _____ on the stage. (bench)
   - ○ **F.** benchs
   - ○ **G.** benchhes
   - ○ **H.** benches
   - ○ **J.** benchies

5. Mr. Lyons even brought some old wooden _____ to use for the feast. (dish)
   - ○ **A.** dishhes
   - ○ **B.** dishies
   - ○ **C.** dishs
   - ○ **D.** dishes

Spelling

Read each sentence. Then find the correct way to spell the missing word. Fill in the circle next to your answer.

1. _____ of my family members make clay pots.
   - ○ **A.** Mowst
   - ○ **B.** Most
   - ○ **C.** Moast
   - ○ **D.** Moste

2. I _____ that my grandmother wants me to learn to make them.
   - ○ **F.** knoe
   - ○ **G.** kno
   - ○ **H.** knoa
   - ○ **J.** know

3. I watch her shape _____ pots out of clay.
   - ○ **A.** three
   - ○ **B.** thre
   - ○ **C.** thrie
   - ○ **D.** theree

4. I help her _____ a cloth over her work table.
   - ○ **F.** speread
   - ○ **G.** spread
   - ○ **H.** sprede
   - ○ **J.** sprid

5. She uses black _____ to make patterns on the white clay.
   - ○ **A.** paynt
   - ○ **B.** pante
   - ○ **C.** paint
   - ○ **D.** paynte

Go on

6. I decide that I _____ like to decorate a pot too.

- ○ **F.** migt
- ○ **G.** might
- ○ **H.** miet
- ○ **J.** mihte

7. Grandmother gives me my _____ pot to decorate.

- ○ **A.** own
- ○ **B.** oan
- ○ **C.** ohne
- ○ **D.** owne

8. I try to make the pattern that I imagine in my _____.

- ○ **F.** miend
- ○ **G.** mighnd
- ○ **H.** mind
- ○ **J.** minde

9. When the paint dries, I _____ up my pot as a gift for my mother.

- ○ **A.** wrapp
- ○ **B.** wrape
- ○ **C.** wrap
- ○ **D.** wrhap

10. I _____ proud that I am learning a family tradition.

- ○ **F.** feal
- ○ **G.** feel
- ○ **H.** feell
- ○ **J.** feale

Vocabulary

Study the guide words and the entry on the dictionary page below. Use the dictionary page to answer Questions 1 through 5. Fill in the circle next to the best answer.

---

parrot / paw

parrot *noun* **1.** A brightly colored tropical bird having a hooked beak: *The parrots in Mexico have lots of yellow feathers.* **2.** Someone who repeats or copies something without understanding. ◆ *verb* To repeat or copy without understanding: *I have to be careful what I do since my brother parrots my actions.*
par•rot (păr′ ət) ◆ *noun, plural* **parrots** ◆ *verb* **parroted, parroting, parrots**

---

1. How many meanings does *parrot* have when used as a verb?
   - ○ **A.** four
   - ○ **B.** three
   - ○ **C.** two
   - ○ **D.** one

2. What is the most common definition of *parrot* as a noun?
   - ○ **F.** someone who repeats or copies something without understanding
   - ○ **G.** a brightly colored tropical bird having a hooked beak
   - ○ **H.** an animal many people keep as a pet
   - ○ **J.** to repeat or copy without understanding

3. Which definition of *parrot* applies to this sentence?

"*Will you please stop <u>parroting</u> everything I say?*"

- ○ **A.** someone who repeats or copies something without understanding
- ○ **B.** to repeat or copy without understanding
- ○ **C.** a brightly colored tropical bird having a hooked beak
- ○ **D.** a pet animal

4. Which of the following words would appear on the page with the guide words **parrot / paw?**

- ○ **F.** parent
- ○ **G.** parquet
- ○ **H.** path
- ○ **J.** pay

5. Which of the following words would **not** appear on the page with the guide words **parrot / paw?**

- ○ **A.** pavement
- ○ **B.** parody
- ○ **C.** patrol
- ○ **D.** passenger

Read each question. Fill in the circle next to the best answer.

6. Which word rhymes with *write?*

- ○ **F.** ride
- ○ **G.** time
- ○ **H.** fine
- ○ **J.** bright

Go on

7. Which word rhymes with *mountain?*

- ○ **A.** fountain
- ○ **B.** scouting
- ○ **C.** maintain
- ○ **D.** mowing

8. Which word belongs in the same word family as *unhappy?*

- ○ **F.** happen
- ○ **G.** helpful
- ○ **H.** happiness
- ○ **J.** hoping

9. Which word belongs in the same word family as *correction?*

- ○ **A.** corner
- ○ **B.** incorrect
- ○ **C.** direction
- ○ **D.** corral

10. Which word belongs in the same word family as *repay?*

- ○ **F.** painting
- ○ **G.** repeat
- ○ **H.** repair
- ○ **J.** payment

Name _____

Grammar

Read each question. Fill in the circle next to the best answer.

1. Which words in this sentence are common nouns?

   The best athletes in the world compete every four years.

   ○ **A.** athletes, compete, years
   ○ **B.** world, every, years
   ○ **C.** athletes, world, years
   ○ **D.** best, compete, years

2. Which word in this sentence is a common noun?

   These special games are called the Olympics.

   ○ **F.** Olympics
   ○ **G.** games
   ○ **H.** special
   ○ **J.** These

3. Which word in this sentence is a proper noun?

   A man in France planned the first games for athletes from around the world.

   ○ **A.** man
   ○ **B.** France
   ○ **C.** games
   ○ **D.** world

4. Which word in this sentence is a common noun?

His full name was Baron Pierre de Coubertin.

- ○ **F.** His
- ○ **G.** full
- ○ **H.** name
- ○ **J.** Pierre de Coubertin

5. Which word in this sentence is a plural noun?

The ruins of an ancient Greek stadium gave him the idea for a worldwide contest.

- ○ **A.** ruins
- ○ **B.** Greek
- ○ **C.** stadium
- ○ **D.** contest

6. Which word in this sentence is a singular noun?

Judges awarded medals to the winners of each contest.

- ○ **F.** Judges
- ○ **G.** medals
- ○ **H.** winners
- ○ **J.** contest

7. Which word in this sentence is a plural noun?

An athlete trains for years to win a medal.

- ○ **A.** athlete
- ○ **B.** years
- ○ **C.** win
- ○ **D.** trains

Choose the correct plural form for the underlined noun in each sentence. Fill in the circle next to the answer you choose.

8. Our <u>country</u> has taken part in the Olympic games since 1896.
   - ○ **F.** countryes
   - ○ **G.** country's
   - ○ **H.** countries
   - ○ **J.** countrys

9. A Russian <u>woman</u> holds the record for the most medals won by one person.
   - ○ **A.** women
   - ○ **B.** womans
   - ○ **C.** woman's
   - ○ **D.** womens

10. Wilma Rudolph was very sick as a <u>child</u>, but she became a successful Olympic athlete.
    - ○ **F.** childes
    - ○ **G.** childrens
    - ○ **H.** children
    - ○ **J.** childs

Name _____

Writing Skills

Read each run-on sentence. Then choose the best way to correct the sentence. Fill in the circle next to the best answer.

1. My family spends every Thanksgiving at a nursing home we help prepare dinner and entertain the people who live there.

   ○ **A.** My family spends every Thanksgiving at a nursing home and we help prepare dinner. And we entertain the people who live there.

   ○ **B.** My family spends every Thanksgiving at a nursing home we help prepare dinner and so we also entertain the people who live there.

   ○ **C.** My family spends every Thanksgiving. It is at a nursing home and we help prepare dinner and entertain the people who live there.

   ○ **D.** My family spends every Thanksgiving at a nursing home. We help prepare dinner and entertain the people who live there.

2. My mom is a great cook she bakes ten pies to take to the celebration and there are never any left.

   ○ **F.** My mom is a great cook. She bakes ten pies to take to the celebration. There are never any left.

   ○ **G.** My mom is a great cook who bakes ten pies.

   ○ **H.** My mom is a great cook and she bakes ten pies to take to the celebration and there are never any left.

   ○ **J.** My mom is a great cook she bakes ten pies. She takes them to the celebration and there are never any left.

3. Dad has a secret recipe for dressing it has been in his family for years and he makes it every year.

- ○ **A.** Dad has a secret recipe for dressing it has been in his family for years. He makes it every year.
- ○ **B.** Dad has a secret recipe for dressing. It has been in his family for years. He makes it every year.
- ○ **C.** Dad has a secret recipe for dressing. And he makes it every year.
- ○ **D.** Dad has a secret recipe for dressing and it has been in his family for years and he makes it every year.

Fill in the circle next to the complete sentence.

4. ○ **F.** Everyone in the family.
    ○ **G.** A special job to do.
    ○ **H.** We take care of everything.
    ○ **J.** Like setting the table, filling the glasses, and serving the food.

5. ○ **A.** Everyone relaxes after a great meal.
    ○ **B.** After enjoying a great meal.
    ○ **C.** A delicious, homemade meal.
    ○ **D.** To enjoy the meal and relax afterwards.

Incredible Stories

Level 3, Theme 3

Theme Skills Test Record

Student _____ Date _____

Student Record Form	Possible Score	Criterion Score	Student Score
Part A: Fantasy and Realism	5	4	
Part B: Following Directions	5	4	
Part C: Drawing Conclusions	5	4	
Part D: Story Structure	5	4	
Part E: Information and Study Skills	5	4	
Part F: Plural Endings	5	4	
Part G: Word Endings	5	4	
Part H: Suffixes	5	4	
Part I: Prefixes	5	4	
Part J: Spelling	10	8	
Part K: Vocabulary	10	8	
Part L: Grammar	10	8	
Part M: Writing Skills	5	4	
TOTAL	80	64	
Total Student Score x 1.25 =			%

Fantasy and Realism

Read this story. Then read each question. Fill in the circle next to the best answer.

A Plane Recess

It was sharing time in Mrs. Soto's kindergarten class. Troy was showing a model airplane he had made. As Troy explained how he made the plane, Angie slowly raised her hand. "Why can't we fly like airplanes?" she asked.

"We can't fly because we don't have wings," answered Troy.

"I wish I had wings," Angie said softly to herself. Just as she spoke, a stretching sound followed by a pop was heard coming from her back. Everyone gasped! Blue wings were growing out of Angie's back! At that same moment, Troy's model plane took off from his hand and flew outside to the playground where, in a puff of smoke, it blew up into a full-sized jumbo jet!

Angie took off from her desk and flew over the crowd that was now gathered around the noisy jet. She circled twice above the plane and the crowd before landing on the plane's wing and climbing through one of its windows. Once Angie was inside, the plane began to rumble and shake and make even more noise. It started to roll forward across the kickball field. Soon, the plane had enough speed and it lifted off the ground. Troy waved at Angie, who was sitting in the pilot's chair.

Mrs. Soto was shocked and unsure of what she should do. She finally realized what time it was. "Class," she said with a big smile, "I believe it's time for recess."

1. What is the **first** clue that this story is a fantasy?
   - ○ **A.** The class has sharing time.
   - ○ **B.** Angie raises her hand to ask a question.
   - ○ **C.** Angie wishes she had wings.
   - ○ **D.** Angie grows wings.

2. Which of these objects could **not** be found at a real school?
   - ○ **F.** a model airplane
   - ○ **G.** a jumbo jet
   - ○ **H.** desks
   - ○ **J.** a kickball field

3. Which of these could really happen?
   - ○ **A.** A boy makes a model plane.
   - ○ **B.** A person grows wings.
   - ○ **C.** A model plane changes into a jumbo jet.
   - ○ **D.** A kindergartner flies a jumbo jet.

4. Which of these could **not** happen at a school?
   - ○ **F.** The teacher says it is time for recess.
   - ○ **G.** Students have sharing time in the classroom.
   - ○ **H.** A jumbo jet takes off from the playground.
   - ○ **J.** A crowd of people gather on the playground.

5. Which of these could really happen?
   - ○ **A.** Troy's model plane takes off from his hand.
   - ○ **B.** Angie lands on the plane's wing.
   - ○ **C.** Angie flies over the crowd.
   - ○ **D.** Mrs. Soto is shocked.

Name _____

Following Directions

Read this story. Then read each question. Fill in the circle next to the best answer.

Giant Stew

Carl had a problem. His giant, Pete, was always hungry. No matter what Carl brought him to eat, Pete always gulped it down in one bite.

One day, Carl heard the giant sigh and say, "Oh, if only I could have one steaming bowl of Giant Stew!" Carl looked in every cookbook he had. Finally he found this recipe.

Giant Stew

1 gallon of olive oil   80 pounds of potatoes
50 onions   40 gallons of tasty broth
25 cloves of garlic   plenty of salt
100 carrots   lots of pepper

    First, mash the garlic and chop up the onions, carrots, and potatoes. Second, heat the oil in a very large tub. Then cook the onions and garlic for 8 minutes. Next, add the carrots, potatoes, and broth. Bring to a boil. Add several big handfuls of salt and pepper. Finally, turn down the heat and cook the stew on low for 8 hours. Serve and make your giant very happy.

Carl followed the directions carefully. When the stew was ready, he called Pete to dinner. When Pete saw the huge tub of giant stew, he was very happy. He lifted Carl up and held him against his giant cheek. "You are the best friend a giant could have," he said.

Go on ⇨

1. How many ingredients does Carl need for making the stew?
   ○ **A.** four
   ○ **B.** eight
   ○ **C.** nine
   ○ **D.** seven

2. What is the third step in making the stew?
   ○ **F.** Boil the broth.
   ○ **G.** Mash the garlic.
   ○ **H.** Add salt.
   ○ **J.** Cook onions and garlic.

3. What does Carl do before he heats the oil?
   ○ **A.** He chops up potatoes.
   ○ **B.** He mixes the carrots, potatoes, and broth.
   ○ **C.** He cooks the stew for eight hours.
   ○ **D.** He adds pepper.

4. When does Carl add the salt and pepper?
   ○ **F.** before he heats the oil
   ○ **G.** after the mixture starts to boil
   ○ **H.** before he adds the broth
   ○ **J.** after he serves the stew

5. What would probably happen if Carl **did not** turn down the heat in the final step?
   ○ **A.** The stew would be perfect.
   ○ **B.** It would still take eight hours for the stew to cook.
   ○ **C.** The giant would no longer be Carl's friend.
   ○ **D.** The stew would boil over the pot and make a huge mess.

Name _____

Drawing Conclusions

Read this story. Then read each question. Fill in the circle next to the best answer.

A Royal Mystery

"They're missing again!" yelled Victor. "He has taken our crowns!"

Victor and Virginia ran down the stone stairs. They saw the burn marks on the wall and smelled the melting paintings. The children ran into the great hall. There they found their parents sitting on their thrones.

"Mother, Father, that naughty beast has taken our crowns again," said Virginia. "May we go after him?"

"Yes, you may, but please do be careful," said Mother. "This game gets him so excited that he can't control his hot breath."

Victor looked into the dining hall and said, "He came through here!" The curtains were burned to ashes, chairs were broken, and the long wooden table was burned down the middle and still smoking.

The children followed the trail of burned and broken furniture through one room after another until it ended at two doors. One door led down to the dungeon in the basement. The other led to the kitchen.

"Where do you think he went?" asked Victor. They stood at the doors. Smoke was curling out from around the edges of the dungeon door.

"I think we're about to get those crowns back!" cried Virginia. "Let's go!"

1. Who are Victor and Virginia?

   ○ **A.** cousins
   ○ **B.** servants
   ○ **C.** brother and sister
   ○ **D.** friends

2. What information lets you know that Victor and Virginia live in a castle?

   ○ **F.** There are paintings on the walls.
   ○ **G.** The stairs are made of stone.
   ○ **H.** There is a long table in the dining room.
   ○ **J.** There are thrones.

3. What information helps you conclude that the beast is friendly?

   ○ **A.** He plays games with the children.
   ○ **B.** He breaks furniture.
   ○ **C.** He runs away from the children.
   ○ **D.** He burns curtains.

4. What conclusion can you make about the beast?

   ○ **F.** He has a tail.
   ○ **G.** He breathes fire.
   ○ **H.** He doesn't like the children.
   ○ **J.** He's very big in size.

5. How do the children know where the beast is at the end?

   ○ **A.** They smell melting paintings.
   ○ **B.** Chairs are broken in the dining hall.
   ○ **C.** The trail leads them to two doors.
   ○ **D.** Smoke is curling out from the dungeon's door.

Name _____

Story Structure

Read this story. Then read each question. Fill in the circle next to the best answer.

Good Boy, Tippy

Mr. and Mrs. Shelby patted Tippy's head as they left. "Be a good dog while we're at work," Mrs. Shelby said. "You know the rules. No messes, no getting on the couch, and absolutely no sleeping on our bed." Tippy whined and whimpered. He did not like the rules at all.

The moment the door closed, Tippy trotted to the family room. He jumped on the couch and looked through magazines. When he found a good recipe in one of the magazines, Tippy headed to the kitchen. He pulled out measuring cups and spoons. He climbed all over the counter and dragged ingredients from the cupboards to a big bowl on the floor. Then he stirred up everything he found with his paw and put his creation in the oven.

After the dish was cooked, Tippy put everything back where it belonged. He ate every last crumb and licked up the floor. When he was through, there were no clues left in the kitchen.

Tippy was now so tired and full that he took a nap on the Shelbys' bed. As always, he woke up when he heard the Shelbys' car door close. He quickly smoothed the sheets and jumped down from the bed.

The Shelbys found Tippy sitting quietly by the door just as they did every day. "Now there's my good dog," said Mrs. Shelby.

1. What is the setting of this story?
    - ○ **A.** the Shelbys' yard
    - ○ **B.** a neighbor's house
    - ○ **C.** Mrs. Shelby's office
    - ○ **D.** the Shelbys' house

2. When does the story take place?
    - ○ **F.** during one night
    - ○ **G.** during the day
    - ○ **H.** during one week
    - ○ **J.** during summer

3. What problem does Tippy have?
    - ○ **A.** He is bored.
    - ○ **B.** He doesn't like his owners' rules.
    - ○ **C.** He sleeps too much.
    - ○ **D.** He doesn't like being left alone.

4. How does Tippy solve his problem?
    - ○ **F.** He thinks of a game to play.
    - ○ **G.** He breaks the rules, but cleans up so no one can tell.
    - ○ **H.** He cooks for his owners.
    - ○ **J.** He waits quietly for his owners to return.

5. How does the story end?
    - ○ **A.** Mrs. Shelby reminds Tippy of the rules.
    - ○ **B.** The Shelbys return to a messy house.
    - ○ **C.** The Shelbys find Tippy sitting by the door.
    - ○ **D.** Tippy eats the food that he made.

Name _____

Information and Study Skills

Study the index and the map. Then read each question.
Fill in the circle next to the best answer.

The United States

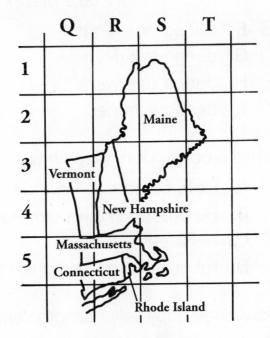

Index	
Alabama	J10
Alaska	A1
Arizona	E12
Arkansas	L11
California	B8
Colorado	F6
Connecticut	R5
Florida	Q14

Map Grid

1. In which grid square would you look to find Arkansas?
   - ○ **A.** E12
   - ○ **B.** L11
   - ○ **C.** Q14
   - ○ **D.** F6

2. What other state is in the same grid square as Connecticut?
   - ○ **F.** Maine
   - ○ **G.** New Hampshire
   - ○ **H.** Vermont
   - ○ **J.** Rhode Island

3. Part of what state is located in the grid square labeled S5?

    ○ **A.** Massachusetts

    ○ **B.** Connecticut

    ○ **C.** New Hampshire

    ○ **D.** Maine

Study the graph. Then read each question. Fill in the circle next to the best answer.

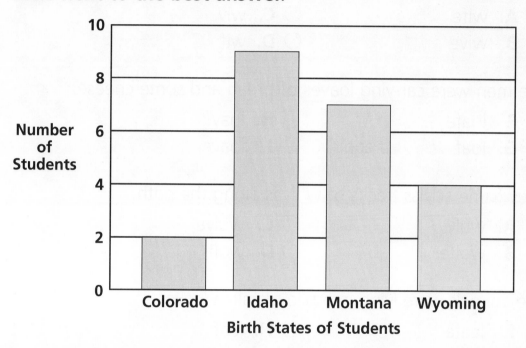

Birth States of Students

4. In which state were the fewest students born?

    ○ **F.** Wyoming

    ○ **G.** Idaho

    ○ **H.** Colorado

    ○ **J.** Montana

5. In which states were more than five students born?

    ○ **A.** Wyoming and Colorado

    ○ **B.** Idaho and Wyoming

    ○ **C.** Montana and Colorado

    ○ **D.** Montana and Idaho

Name _____

Plural Endings

Read each sentence. Choose the correct base word for each underlined word. Fill in the circle next to your answer.

1. The men waved goodbye to their <u>wives</u> and left on their walk.
   - ○ **A.** wife
   - ○ **B.** wive
   - ○ **C.** wiv
   - ○ **D.** wif

2. The men were carrying <u>loaves</u> of bread and some cheese.
   - ○ **F.** loafe
   - ○ **G.** loaf
   - ○ **H.** loav
   - ○ **J.** loave

3. They came across tracks of <u>wolves</u> along the path.
   - ○ **A.** wolv
   - ○ **B.** wolfe
   - ○ **C.** wolve
   - ○ **D.** wolf

4. The animals were lying in a pile of fallen <u>leaves</u>.
   - ○ **F.** leafe
   - ○ **G.** leav
   - ○ **H.** leaf
   - ○ **J.** leafs

5. "Don't you wonder what their <u>lives</u> are like?" one of the animals said.
   - ○ **A.** live
   - ○ **B.** liv
   - ○ **C.** lif
   - ○ **D.** life

G Name _____

Word Endings

Read each sentence. Choose the correct base word and ending for each underlined word. Fill in the circle next to your answer.

1. The contest was to decide who had the <u>clearest</u> singing voice.
   - ○ **A.** clear + st
   - ○ **B.** clea + rest
   - ○ **C.** clear + est
   - ○ **D.** cleare + st

2. The pig's voice was <u>smoother</u> than the others' voices.
   - ○ **F.** smoot + her
   - ○ **G.** smooth + er
   - ○ **H.** smoothe + r
   - ○ **J.** smoo + ther

3. The little mouse had the <u>quietest</u> singing voice.
   - ○ **A.** quie + test
   - ○ **B.** quiete + st
   - ○ **C.** quiet + st
   - ○ **D.** quiet + est

Read each sentence. Choose the definition of the underlined word. Fill in the circle next to your answer.

4. The horse's voice was <u>louder</u> than the rabbit's voice.
   - ○ **F.** is loud
   - ○ **G.** more loud
   - ○ **H.** not loud
   - ○ **J.** most loud

5. The owl had the <u>hardest</u> decision in choosing a winner.
   - ○ **A.** most hard
   - ○ **B.** not hard
   - ○ **C.** was hard
   - ○ **D.** more hard

Name _____

Suffixes

Read each sentence. Choose the correct base word and ending for each underlined word. Fill in the circle next to your answer.

1. This morning, my sister did not look <u>healthy</u>.
   - ○ **A.** healt + hy
   - ○ **B.** heal + thy
   - ○ **C.** health + y
   - ○ **D.** health + ly

2. Her face was <u>completely</u> covered with green polka dots.
   - ○ **F.** complete + ly
   - ○ **G.** complet + ely
   - ○ **H.** comple + tely
   - ○ **J.** completel + y

3. My dad said, "We must act <u>quickly</u>."
   - ○ **A.** quickl + y
   - ○ **B.** quick + ly
   - ○ **C.** qui + ckly
   - ○ **D.** quic + kly

Read each sentence. Choose the meaning of the underlined word. Fill in the circle next to your answer.

4. He found an old, <u>dusty</u> cookbook and made her some honey pudding.
   - ○ **F.** without dust
   - ○ **G.** more dust
   - ○ **H.** most dust
   - ○ **J.** full of dust

5. My sister's face returned <u>slowly</u> to its normal color.
   - ○ **A.** most slow
   - ○ **B.** full of slowness
   - ○ **C.** in a slow way
   - ○ **D.** more slow

Name _____

Prefixes

Read each sentence. Choose the correct word to complete each sentence. Fill in the circle next to your answer.

1. "You never eat when I tell you to! Why do you always _____ me?" Anna asked her dog.
- ○ **A.** disable
- ○ **B.** unlock
- ○ **C.** disobey
- ○ **D.** recover

2. "Simple," said Shadow. "I _____ dry dog food."
- ○ **F.** dislike
- ○ **G.** displease
- ○ **H.** unlike
- ○ **J.** recall

3. "I didn't know. I was completely _____," said Anna.
- ○ **A.** unhappy
- ○ **B.** unaware
- ○ **C.** unbroken
- ○ **D.** nonsense

4. "What happened?" she asked. "You used to eat _____, all the time."
- ○ **F.** uncertain
- ○ **G.** unclear
- ○ **H.** nonstop
- ○ **J.** nonsense

5. "The label doesn't say what's in the food. I don't like being _____ of what I'm eating," said Shadow.
- ○ **A.** dishonest
- ○ **B.** recycle
- ○ **C.** unafraid
- ○ **D.** unsure

Name _____

Spelling

Read each sentence. Then find the correct way to spell the missing word. Fill in the circle next to your answer.

1. The strangest day of Pablo's life started with _____, blue skies.
    - ○ **A.** cler
    - ○ **B.** clere
    - ○ **C.** cleer
    - ○ **D.** clear

2. He _____ something was wrong when a purple cloud filled his bedroom.
    - ○ **F.** new
    - ○ **G.** nue
    - ○ **H.** knew
    - ○ **J.** knoo

3. When he tried to get dressed, his shirt and _____ ran away from him.
    - ○ **A.** jeans
    - ○ **B.** geans
    - ○ **C.** geens
    - ○ **D.** jeens

4. As he walked outside, he heard a loud _____ of thunder.
    - ○ **F.** krak
    - ○ **G.** crack
    - ○ **H.** crak
    - ○ **J.** krack

5. The sky began to turn _____, and Pablo got a very strange feeling.
    - ○ **A.** dark
    - ○ **B.** derk
    - ○ **C.** durk
    - ○ **D.** dahrk

Go on

6. Suddenly, the whole front _____ swelled up into a big, grassy lump.

○ **F.** laun   ○ **H.** lon

○ **G.** lawn   ○ **J.** lahn

7. Pablo watched the lump _____ into a giant green caterpillar.

○ **A.** tern   ○ **C.** tirne

○ **B.** turne   ○ **D.** turn

8. The caterpillar tried to _____ under the fence.

○ **F.** squeeze   ○ **H.** sqeeze

○ **G.** skweeze   ○ **J.** scueeze

9. When it got stuck, the caterpillar made a scared, crying _____.

○ **A.** sownd   ○ **C.** sound

○ **B.** sawnd   ○ **D.** saund

10. Pablo bent down to help, but he didn't _____ crying anymore.

○ **F.** here   ○ **H.** hear

○ **G.** heer   ○ **J.** heir

Name _____

Vocabulary

Study the pronunciation key, the words, and their pronunciations below. Read each question. Fill in the circle next to the best answer.

ă pat	ĭ pit	oi oil
ā pay	ī ride	ŏŏ book
â care	î fierce	ōō boot
ä father	ŏ pot	ou bout
ě pet	ō go	ŭ cut
ē be	ô paw, for	û fur

spring (sprĭng)   **work** (wûrk)

1. Which word in the pronunciation key shows how to say the vowel sound in *spring*?
   - ○ **A.** pit
   - ○ **B.** father
   - ○ **C.** fierce
   - ○ **D.** pet

2. Which word in the pronunciation key shows how to say the vowel sound in *work*?
   - ○ **F.** care
   - ○ **G.** fur
   - ○ **H.** for
   - ○ **J.** pot

 Go on

spring *verb* **1.** To leap in one quick movement: *She sprang from her seat.* **2.** To appear quickly: *New stores seem to spring up everyday.* ◆*noun* **1.** An object made from elastic or soft metal that keeps its original shape after being pulled and twisted. **2.** The act of leaping in one quick movement. **3.** A natural water flow: *The bridge on the trail crossed a spring.* **4.** The time of year between winter and summer.

3. Which is the correct meaning of *spring* in this sentence?

   The stuffed animals spring out of the toy box and onto the floor.

   ○ **A.** a natural water flow
   ○ **B.** to appear quickly
   ○ **C.** the act of leaping in one quick movement
   ○ **D.** to leap in one quick movement

4. Which is the correct meaning of *spring* in this sentence?

   Bear jumped up and down on a spring.

   ○ **F.** the act of leaping in one quick movement
   ○ **G.** to leap in one quick movement
   ○ **H.** an object made from elastic or soft metal that keeps its original shape after being pulled and twisted
   ○ **J.** to appear quickly

5. Which is the correct meaning of *spring* in this sentence?

Bear's spring into the air ended with a crash.

- ○ **A.** to appear quickly
- ○ **B.** a natural water flow
- ○ **C.** the time of year between winter and summer
- ○ **D.** the act of leaping in one quick movement

Study the thesaurus entry below. Read each sentence. Choose the best word to replace the word *hit*. Fill in the circle next to your answer.

> **hit,** slap, pound, punch, smash, kick. All of these verbs can mean "to touch something very hard."

6. Rita hit the door to her room with her foot.
- ○ **F.** kicked
- ○ **G.** pounded
- ○ **H.** punched
- ○ **J.** smashed

7. The door opened suddenly and accidentally hit Bear on the nose.
- ○ **A.** kicked
- ○ **B.** punched
- ○ **C.** slapped
- ○ **D.** smashed

Read each sentence. Choose the correct meaning for each underlined word. Fill in the circle next to your answer.

8. Rita said she was sorry and covered Bear's nose with <u>gauze</u>.
   - ○ **F.** a blanket
   - ○ **G.** a sticker
   - ○ **H.** a bandage
   - ○ **J.** a hat

9. Bear's face had a look of <u>agony</u>.
   - ○ **A.** happiness
   - ○ **B.** great pain
   - ○ **C.** disorder
   - ○ **D.** glitter

10. To <u>atone</u> for hurting Bear, Rita took all the animals out for ice cream in her toy plane.
    - ○ **F.** forget
    - ○ **G.** remind
    - ○ **H.** travel
    - ○ **J.** make up

Grammar

Read each sentence. Choose the correct possessive to replace the underlined words. Fill in the circle next to the best answer.

1. The twins spent a strange morning in <u>the garden of their uncle</u>.
   ○ **A.** their uncles' garden   ○ **C.** their uncles garden
   ○ **B.** their uncle's garden   ○ **D.** their uncle garden's

2. <u>The favorite place for the twins</u> was the lily pond.
   ○ **F.** The twins' favorite place   ○ **H.** The twins favorite place
   ○ **G.** The twin's favorite place   ○ **J.** The twins favorite place's

3. But that morning, they thought they heard <u>the voice of a person</u> calling.
   ○ **A.** a person voice   ○ **C.** a persons voice
   ○ **B.** a persons' voices   ○ **D.** a person's voice

Find the verb in each sentence. Fill in the circle next to the word you choose.

4. Then the twins heard the voice again.
   ○ **F.** twins   ○ **H.** voice
   ○ **G.** heard   ○ **J.** again

5. The voice grew louder and angrier.
   ○ **A.** voice   ○ **C.** grew
   ○ **B.** louder   ○ **D.** angrier

Go on

Read each sentence. Choose the correct verb to complete each sentence. Fill in the circle next to the best answer.

6. "I _____ a new place to live right now," said the voice.
   - ○ **F.** wanted
   - ○ **G.** want
   - ○ **H.** wants
   - ○ **J.** wanting

7. The twins went over and _____ behind the trees and bushes.
   - ○ **A.** look
   - ○ **B.** looking
   - ○ **C.** looks
   - ○ **D.** looked

8. "I _____ you in silver coins tomorrow for a new place to live today," said the voice.
   - ○ **F.** paying
   - ○ **G.** paid
   - ○ **H.** will pay
   - ○ **J.** pays

9. Then the twins _____ a peacock in a tree.
   - ○ **A.** noticed
   - ○ **B.** noticing
   - ○ **C.** notices
   - ○ **D.** will notice

10. "Too many birds _____ in this tree with me right now!"
   - ○ **F.** lived
   - ○ **G.** live
   - ○ **H.** will live
   - ○ **J.** lives

Name _____

Writing Skills

Read each sentence. Choose the sentence that shows the correct way to use commas. Fill in the circle next to your answer.

1. ○ **A.** Michael, Brad is on the phone for, you.
   ○ **B.** Michael Brad is, on the phone for you.
   ○ **C.** Michael Brad, is on the phone for you.
   ○ **D.** Michael, Brad is on the phone for you.

2. ○ **F.** I'm sure Brad, that we can solve the problem.
   ○ **G.** I'm sure, Brad that we can solve the problem.
   ○ **H.** I'm sure, Brad, that we can solve the problem.
   ○ **J.** I'm, sure Brad that we can solve the problem.

3. ○ **A.** I don't think you understand what's happening, Michael.
   ○ **B.** I, don't think you understand what's happening Michael.
   ○ **C.** I don't think, you understand what's happening Michael.
   ○ **D.** I don't think you understand what's happening Michael.

Read each sentence. Choose the sentence that has the correct punctuation and capitalization. Fill in the circle next to your answer.

4. ○ **F.** Michael said. "I'll be right over."
   ○ **G.** Michael said, "I'll be right over."
   ○ **H.** Michael said, i'll be right over.
   ○ **J.** Michael said "I'll be right over."

5. ○ **A.** "I'm sorry," the woman at the door said. "No one named Brad lives here."
   ○ **B.** "I'm sorry" The woman at the door said, "No one named Brad lives here."
   ○ **C.** "I'm sorry," the woman at the door said "no one named Brad lives here."
   ○ **D.** I'm sorry, the woman at the door said. "No one named Brad lives here."

Animal Habitats

Level 3, Theme 4

Theme Skills Test Record

Student _____   Date _____

Student Record Form	Possible Score	Criterion Score	Student Score
Part A: Fact and Opinion	5	4	
Part B: Compare and Contrast	5	4	
Part C: Making Judgments	5	4	
Part D: Information and Study Skills	5	4	
Part E: Syllabication	5	4	
Part F: Word Endings	5	4	
Part G: Prefixes and Suffixes	5	4	
Part H: Spelling	10	8	
Part I: Vocabulary	10	8	
Part J: Grammar	10	8	
Part K: Writing Skills	5	4	
TOTAL	70	56	
Total Student Score x 1.43 =			%

Name _____

Fact and Opinion

Read this story. Then read each question. Fill in the circle next to the best answer.

Behaving Like an Animal

Have you ever seen a squirrel or a rat? How about a nutria? Nutrias are rodents, which puts them in the same category as squirrels, rats, and even beavers. They are cute animals that have brown fur and long tails.

People brought nutrias to Europe and North America from South America. They hoped to raise nutrias for their fur. Yet, this was not a smart idea. Not enough money was made from nutrias' fur, so the people gave up. Nutrias, however, learned how to survive in their new homelands.

Unfortunately, nutrias have become real pests in many places. They cause leaks in dams by digging holes. They destroy water plants. Nutrias can even destroy crops of rice and sugar cane.

Because they are so cute, people think nutrias are harmless. Yet, these animals are a very big problem. Many people don't want them around anymore.

1. Which of the following statements gives an opinion?
   - ○ **A.** Nutrias have brown fur.
   - ○ **B.** Nutrias are cute.
   - ○ **C.** Nutrias are rodents.
   - ○ **D.** Nutrias came from South America.

Go on

2. Which of these states a fact?
- ○ **F.** Nutrias are cute.
- ○ **G.** Raising nutrias for their fur is not a smart idea.
- ○ **H.** Nutrias are a problem.
- ○ **J.** Nutrias can destroy crops of rice and sugar cane.

3. Which word tells you that this statement gives an opinion?

People think nutrias look harmless.
- ○ **A.** think
- ○ **B.** people
- ○ **C.** harmless
- ○ **D.** look

4. How can you tell that this statement tells a fact?

These animals cause leaks in dams by digging holes.
- ○ **F.** It is written by the author.
- ○ **G.** You can ask people who take care of dams if this is true.
- ○ **H.** Everyone knows that when a dam has a hole, it leaks.
- ○ **J.** It isn't a fact.

5. Which of these statements shows the author's opinion about nutrias?
- ○ **A.** Nutrias are rodents.
- ○ **B.** Nutrias learned how to survive.
- ○ **C.** Nutrias are a very big problem.
- ○ **D.** Nutrias can even destroy crops of rice.

Name _____

Compare and Contrast

Read this passage. Then read each question. Fill in the circle next to the best answer.

Crocodiles and Alligators

Can you tell a crocodile from an alligator? They are alike in some ways. Yet, in other ways, they are very different.

Both animals are covered with scales and have backbones. They have short legs and long, powerful tails. Also, baby crocodiles and alligators both hatch from eggs.

Both crocodiles and alligators are very dangerous and very strong hunters. Both eat fish and small animals, and they can even attack people, though that is rare. These two animals have strong jaws and many sharp teeth. They also have eyes high on their head so they can see while they float in the water. Both can be found in hot, damp places like swamps.

Crocodiles and alligators are different in certain ways. For example, a crocodile's snout, or the part of its head that sticks outward and includes its nose and mouth, is pointed at the end. The snout of an alligator is broad and rounder. Also, crocodiles like muddy, shallow water, while alligators are usually found in deeper water.

1. Which is true about both crocodiles and alligators?
   ○ **A.** They have backbones.
   ○ **B.** Their eyes are set low on the sides of their heads.
   ○ **C.** They cannot float on water.
   ○ **D.** They live in deep water.

2. How is a crocodile's body different from an alligator's?

- ○ **F.** Crocodiles have short legs.
- ○ **G.** Crocodiles have a short tail.
- ○ **H.** Crocodiles have sharper teeth.
- ○ **J.** Crocodiles have pointed snouts.

3. How are crocodiles and alligators alike?

- ○ **A.** They both like to attack people.
- ○ **B.** Their bodies are covered with scales.
- ○ **C.** They have only a couple of sharp teeth.
- ○ **D.** They only eat fish.

4. How are crocodiles and alligators different?

- ○ **F.** Only crocodiles eat small animals.
- ○ **G.** Only alligators have strong jaws.
- ○ **H.** Only alligators have rounded snouts.
- ○ **J.** Only crocodiles live in water.

5. What do alligators do that crocodiles do not?

- ○ **A.** live in hot, damp places
- ○ **B.** lay eggs
- ○ **C.** live in deeper water
- ○ **D.** eat fish

Name _____

Making Judgments

Read this passage. Then read each question. Fill in the circle next to the best answer.

Sidewalk Rescue

Toby and Elena were just beginning their walk home from school. "Look!" said Toby. "There's a baby bird on the sidewalk!"

"Do you see how it's trying to flap its wings?" asked Elena. "Maybe its mother is teaching it how to fly." The children turned in circles looking for the bird's mother, but there were no other birds around.

"Hey, there's the nest!" Toby called out. He pointed to a small clump of grass and twigs in a nearby bush. "I think we should put the bird back in its nest," he said.

Elena frowned. "I don't think that's a good idea. Baby birds are not very strong. What if you hurt it?"

"If I don't move it, its mother may not find it," said Toby.

"Just stay here and watch it. I'll go get a teacher to help us." Elena headed toward the school building.

As Toby was deciding what to do, he noticed a cat watching from across the street. It quietly moved closer and closer as it stared at the tiny bird. "I can't just leave the bird here on the sidewalk," Toby thought. "It's too dangerous."

Toby wrapped his hands in his scarf and gently picked up the helpless bird as the cat ran toward it. Toby placed the bird in the nest, and the cat stopped at the bush, looked up at the nest, and licked its lips. "Don't worry, little bird," said Toby. "You're safe now."

1. What do Toby and Elena disagree about?
   - ○ **A.** whether to move the bird's nest
   - ○ **B.** who the cat belongs to
   - ○ **C.** how to find the missing mother bird
   - ○ **D.** how to help the baby bird

2. What is good about Toby's solution?
   - ○ **F.** It will show the baby bird how to fly.
   - ○ **G.** It might hurt the bird.
   - ○ **H.** It will keep the bird out of danger.
   - ○ **J.** It will make the mother bird return.

3. Why might Elena's idea to get an adult's help be best?
   - ○ **A.** An adult can scare the cat away.
   - ○ **B.** Adults are not afraid of animals.
   - ○ **C.** An adult may know how to handle the bird.
   - ○ **D.** An adult can teach the bird to fly.

4. What might be bad about Toby's idea?
   - ○ **F.** Elena might not come back.
   - ○ **G.** Toby might hurt the bird.
   - ○ **H.** Toby might not find the nest.
   - ○ **J.** The bird might fly away.

5. What might be bad about Elena's idea?
   - ○ **A.** The teacher might not believe Elena.
   - ○ **B.** The baby bird might fly away before Elena comes back.
   - ○ **C.** The cat might get the bird before Elena returns with an adult.
   - ○ **D.** Toby might hurt the bird.

Name _____

Information and Study Skills

Read each question. Then fill in the circle next to the best answer.

1. What should you keep in mind when you do research on the Internet?

   ○ **A.** The information may not always be correct.
   ○ **B.** The Internet gives too much information.
   ○ **C.** The Internet is only made up of opinions.
   ○ **D.** Using the Internet is the best way to do research.

2. Once you find an Internet search engine to use, what should you do?

   ○ **F.** Compare the information to an encyclopedia.
   ○ **G.** Click on the list of sites that appears on the screen.
   ○ **H.** Type in a useful keyword.
   ○ **J.** Start your search over.

3. Which is the best topic to search under to find out what polar bears eat?

   ○ **A.** Food
   ○ **B.** Polar bears
   ○ **C.** Animals
   ○ **D.** Animal health

4. In searching the Internet for information on polar bears, which related topic are you likely to come across?

- ○ **F.** cold weather clothes
- ○ **G.** snow games
- ○ **H.** weather
- ○ **J.** grizzly bears

5. How are electronic encyclopedias different from the Internet?

- ○ **A.** The Internet is always faster.
- ○ **B.** Information in encyclopedias is usually correct.
- ○ **C.** Topics can only be used for an Internet search.
- ○ **D.** The "Search" feature works only with encyclopedias.

E

Name _____

Syllabication

Read each sentence. Then choose the best way to divide each underlined word into syllables. Fill in the circle next to the best answer.

1. Leo and Maria went on a hike into the <u>wilderness</u>.
    - ○ **A.** wi • lde • rness
    - ○ **B.** wil • dern • ess
    - ○ **C.** wil • der • ness
    - ○ **D.** wild • ern • ess

2. They were <u>looking</u> for wildlife.
    - ○ **F.** lo • oking
    - ○ **G.** look • ing
    - ○ **H.** loo • king
    - ○ **J.** l • ook • ing

Choose the best word to complete each sentence. Fill in the circle next to your answer.

3. Leo heard a loud and _____ noise like a knock.
    - ○ **A.** confusion
    - ○ **B.** confuse
    - ○ **C.** confused
    - ○ **D.** confusing

4. "That's the beak of a _____ hitting a tree," said Maria.
    - ○ **F.** wooded
    - ○ **G.** wooden
    - ○ **H.** woodpecker
    - ○ **J.** woodwork

5. "It must be _____ a hole for its nest," she said.
    - ○ **A.** creating
    - ○ **B.** creation
    - ○ **C.** create
    - ○ **D.** created

STOP

Name _____

Word Endings

Read each sentence. Choose the base word and ending for each underlined word. Fill in the circle next to the best answer.

1. Our class was <u>studying</u> all about birds.
   - ○ **A.** study + ing
   - ○ **B.** studi + ing
   - ○ **C.** stud + ing
   - ○ **D.** stud + yng

2. We were <u>invited</u> to the local zoo by the zookeeper.
   - ○ **F.** invit + ed
   - ○ **G.** invite + ed
   - ○ **H.** invite + d
   - ○ **J.** invit + ted

3. While we looked around, we spotted a flock of geese <u>flying</u> over the zoo.
   - ○ **A.** fly + ing
   - ○ **B.** fli + ing
   - ○ **C.** fly + ng
   - ○ **D.** fli + ying

4. Suddenly, we <u>noticed</u> an injured goose on the ground.
   - ○ **F.** notice + d
   - ○ **G.** notic + ed
   - ○ **H.** noti + ced
   - ○ **J.** notice + ed

5. Our teacher <u>hurried</u> to find the zookeeper.
   - ○ **A.** hurrie + d
   - ○ **B.** hurr + yed
   - ○ **C.** hurry + ed
   - ○ **D.** hurri + ed

Name _____

Prefixes and Suffixes

**Read each sentence. Then find the meaning of each
underlined word. Fill in the circle next to the best
answer.**

1. Mr. Lansing was a wheat <u>farmer</u>.
   - ○ **A.** full of farming
   - ○ **B.** farm again
   - ○ **C.** the opposite of farm
   - ○ **D.** one who farms

2. He planned to clean his shed and <u>rearrange</u> his tools.
   - ○ **F.** the opposite of arrange
   - ○ **G.** arrange again
   - ○ **H.** in an arranged way
   - ○ **J.** full of arranging

3. He found an <u>untidy</u> pile of rags and paper in a corner.
   - ○ **A.** in a tidy way
   - ○ **B.** tidy again
   - ○ **C.** full of tidy
   - ○ **D.** not tidy

4. When he moved the pile, several mice <u>hurriedly</u> scampered away.
   - ○ **F.** in a hurried way
   - ○ **G.** the opposite of hurried
   - ○ **H.** hurried again
   - ○ **J.** one who hurries

5. The farmer was <u>careful</u> to patch all the holes he could find.
   - ○ **A.** one who cares
   - ○ **B.** caring again
   - ○ **C.** full of care
   - ○ **D.** the opposite of care

Name _____

Spelling

Read each sentence. Then find the correct way to spell the missing word. Fill in the circle next to your answer.

1. The forest ranger and her _____, Diana, followed some animal tracks.
   - ○ **A.** helpir
   - ○ **B.** helpper
   - ○ **C.** helpere
   - ○ **D.** helper

2. They spotted a grizzly _____ near the river.
   - ○ **F.** bare
   - ○ **G.** bere
   - ○ **H.** bear
   - ○ **J.** bair

3. After she caught a _____ of salmon, the grizzly lifted her head toward them.
   - ○ **A.** pear
   - ○ **B.** pair
   - ○ **C.** pere
   - ○ **D.** paire

4. "That grizzly doesn't look too _____," said the ranger.
   - ○ **F.** friendlie
   - ○ **G.** friendley
   - ○ **H.** friendly
   - ○ **J.** frendly

5. "Maybe she will change her mind," said Diana, but she didn't sound very _____.
   - ○ **A.** hopful
   - ○ **B.** hopeful
   - ○ **C.** hopefully
   - ○ **D.** hopefull

6. When the grizzly turned away, Diana _____ with relief.

   ○ **F.** smilyed   ○ **H.** smileed

   ○ **G.** smiled   ○ **J.** smyled

7. "That gave me quite a _____," she said.

   ○ **A.** scare   ○ **C.** scair

   ○ **B.** scear   ○ **D.** scayre

8. "I'm glad we are both _____," said the ranger. "I wonder why the grizzly turned around."

   ○ **F.** unnhurt   ○ **H.** inhurt

   ○ **G.** unhurt   ○ **J.** enhurt

9. "There are two cubs over there," said Diana _____.

   ○ **A.** grining   ○ **C.** grinnin

   ○ **B.** grinning   ○ **D.** grininng

10. "We'd better leave now. She'll do anything to protect her _____!" said the ranger.

   ○ **F.** babees   ○ **H.** babbies

   ○ **G.** babyes   ○ **J.** babies

Name _____

Vocabulary

Study the dictionary entry below. Read each question. Fill in the circle next to the best answer.

> **fly**¹ *verb* **1.** To move over air using wings: *Not every bird can fly.* **2.** To move through air in an aircraft: *I flew to Idaho to see my sister.* **3.** In baseball, to hit a ball high in the air: *He flew out to centerfield to end the game.* **4.** To move quickly: *Summertime always seems to fly by.* ◆ *noun* **1.** In baseball, a ball hit high in the air. **2.** A flap of cloth that covers a zipper.
> **fly**¹ (flī) ◆ *verb* **flew** or **flied** (for sense 3), **flown** or **flied** (for sense 3), **flying** ◆ *noun, plural* **flies**
>
> **fly**² *noun* An insect with wings, especially one in the group that includes the housefly.
> **fly**² (flī) ◆ *noun, plural* **flies**

1. Which part of speech is *fly* in this sentence?

   The leopard <u>flew</u> by us so fast we couldn't get a picture of it.

   ○ **A.** an adjective   ○ **C.** a verb
   ○ **B.** a pronunciation   ○ **D.** a noun

2. Which part of speech is *fly* in this sentence?

   Throughout our tour of Africa, we were bothered by <u>flies</u> buzzing around us.

   ○ **F.** a base word   ○ **H.** a verb
   ○ **G.** an adverb   ○ **J.** a noun

3. Which part of speech is *fly* in this sentence?

There were so many bugs that I just wished they would all fly away.

- ○ **A.** a plural
- ○ **B.** a verb
- ○ **C.** an adjective
- ○ **D.** a noun

4. What is the meaning of *fly* in this sentence?

We saw many birds during our trip, even some that couldn't fly.

- ○ **F.** To move through air in an aircraft
- ○ **G.** A flap of cloth that covers a zipper
- ○ **H.** To move over air using wings
- ○ **J.** To move quickly

5. What is the meaning of *fly* in this sentence?

We were in such a rugged part of the country that we had to fly in by helicopter.

- ○ **A.** To move through air in an aircraft
- ○ **B.** To move quickly
- ○ **C.** An insect with wings, especially one in the group that includes the housefly
- ○ **D.** In baseball, to hit a ball high in the air

6. What is the meaning of *fly* in this sentence?

At night it was so cold that I had to close the fly on my sleeping bag to keep the air from going through the zipper.

- ○ **F.** In baseball, a ball hit high in the air
- ○ **G.** A flap of cloth that covers a zipper
- ○ **H.** To move over air using wings
- ○ **J.** To move through air in an aircraft

Go on ▷

7. What is the meaning of *fly* in this sentence?

During the night, I dreamt of hitting a <u>fly</u> over the fielder's head to win the game.

- ○ **A.** To move quickly
- ○ **B.** An insect with wings, especially one in the group that includes the housefly
- ○ **C.** In baseball, to hit a ball high in the air
- ○ **D.** In baseball, a ball hit high in the air

8. Which form of *fly* best completes this sentence?

"I woke up with all these _____ buzzing around my head."

- ○ **F.** flies
- ○ **G.** flown
- ○ **H.** fly
- ○ **J.** flew

9. Which form of *fly* best completes this sentence?

"So how big was the plane _____ home?" my friend asked.

- ○ **A.** flied
- ○ **B.** flies
- ○ **C.** flying
- ○ **D.** flew

10. Which form of *fly* best completes this sentence?

"It was huge. And we saw many birds _____ by the window!"

- ○ **F.** flown
- ○ **G.** fly
- ○ **H.** flied
- ○ **J.** flew

Name _____

Grammar

Read each group of sentences. Choose the sentence that is written correctly. Fill in the circle next to the best answer.

1. ○ **A.** I is very interested in whales.
    ○ **B.** I am very interested in whales.
    ○ **C.** I are very interested in whales.
    ○ **D.** I were very interested in whales.

2. ○ **F.** I has read all about interesting ocean animals.
    ○ **G.** I have reading all about interesting ocean animals.
    ○ **H.** I had reading all about interesting ocean animals.
    ○ **J.** I have read all about interesting ocean animals.

3. ○ **A.** Last summer was very exciting.
    ○ **B.** Last summer are very exciting.
    ○ **C.** Last summer is very exciting.
    ○ **D.** Last summer were very exciting.

4. ○ **F.** We am on a boat trip.
    ○ **G.** We is on a boat trip.
    ○ **H.** We were on a boat trip.
    ○ **J.** We was on a boat trip.

Read each sentence. Choose the answer that best completes the sentence. Fill in the circle next to the correct answer.

5. "I _____ several whales in this area," said the boat captain.
   - ○ **A.** has seen
   - ○ **B.** have saw
   - ○ **C.** have seen
   - ○ **D.** has saw

6. "We _____ for over two hours," I complained.
   - ○ **F.** has sailed
   - ○ **G.** have sailed
   - ○ **H.** has sail
   - ○ **J.** have sail

7. Suddenly, something large and dark _____ up out of the water.
   - ○ **A.** came
   - ○ **B.** come
   - ○ **C.** had came
   - ○ **D.** has came

8. My brother _____ the whale before anyone else.
   - ○ **F.** have seen
   - ○ **G.** seen
   - ○ **H.** had saw
   - ○ **J.** saw

9. My father _____ me the binoculars.
   - ○ **A.** have gaved
   - ○ **B.** gave
   - ○ **C.** has gived
   - ○ **D.** given

10. Right then, I knew I _____ the best vacation ever.
    - ○ **F.** had took
    - ○ **G.** have take
    - ○ **H.** had taken
    - ○ **J.** had take

Name _____

Writing Skills

Read each question. Fill in the circle next to the best answer.

1. How could you change this sentence to a command?

   Can you see the baby deer across the meadow?

   ○ **A.** Do you see the baby deer across the meadow?
   ○ **B.** There is a baby deer across the meadow.
   ○ **C.** What a beautiful baby deer!
   ○ **D.** Look at the baby deer across the meadow.

2. How could you change this sentence to a question?

   I wonder if you can see the fawn's mother.

   ○ **F.** I do not see the fawn's mother.
   ○ **G.** Find the fawn's mother.
   ○ **H.** Can you see the fawn's mother?
   ○ **J.** What a lonely fawn with no mother!

3. How could you change this sentence to an exclamation?

   I see a buck with large antlers.

   ○ **A.** What large antlers that buck has!
   ○ **B.** Have you ever seen such large antlers?
   ○ **C.** Those are very large antlers.
   ○ **D.** Look at that buck's antlers.

4. How could you change this sentence to a statement?

Do you hear that rustling noise?

- ○ **F.** What is that rustling noise?
- ○ **G.** What a strange noise that is!
- ○ **H.** I think I hear a rustling noise.
- ○ **J.** Listen to that rustling noise.

5. How could you change this sentence to a command?

The deer run very gracefully.

- ○ **A.** Have you ever seen animals run more gracefully?
- ○ **B.** Watch how gracefully the deer run.
- ○ **C.** I think the deer run very gracefully.
- ○ **D.** How gracefully the deer run!

Voyagers

Level 3, Theme 5

Theme Skills Test Record

Student _____ Date _____

Student Record Form	Possible Score	Criterion Score	Student Score
Part A: Making Inferences	5	4	
Part B: Predicting Outcomes	5	4	
Part C: Text Organization	5	4	
Part D: Information and Study Skills	5	4	
Part E: Suffixes	5	4	
Part F: Possessives	5	4	
Part G: VCCV Pattern	5	4	
Part H: Spelling	10	8	
Part I: Vocabulary	10	8	
Part J: Grammar	10	8	
Part K: Writing Skills	5	4	
TOTAL	70	56	
Total Student Score x 1.43 =			%

Name _____

Making Inferences

Read this story. Then read each question. Fill in the circle next to the best answer.

A First-Time Traveler

Debbie was about to fly on an airplane for the first time. She frowned as she watched the big planes land and take off. She was trying to imagine how it would feel to leave the ground where it was safe. Debbie stepped a little closer to her father.

"You're squeezing my hand pretty tightly," he said with a smile.

Finally, it was time to board the plane. As they walked down the crowded aisle of the airplane, Debbie lost hold of her father's hand. "Dad, wait for me!"

Her father reached back and took her hand. "Don't worry. I'm right here." They walked past three more rows. "Here are our seats. Would you like to sit by the window?"

Debbie sat by the window and clenched her fists tightly. She kept her eyes closed while the plane took off. After they were in the air, she opened her eyes. The ride was very smooth. It felt just like riding in a car. She looked out the window and saw buildings, roads, and farms through the clouds. It was fun to see how small things looked. Debbie rested back against her seat and smiled at her father.

He gave her a wink and squeezed her hand. "Grandma will be very glad to see you."

"Maybe we could fly out to see her every summer," said Debbie.

1. Which is a clue that shows how Debbie feels while waiting to board the plane?
   - ○ **A.** She is frowning.
   - ○ **B.** She watches the planes take off.
   - ○ **C.** She stands near her father.
   - ○ **D.** She holds her father's hand.

2. Which word best describes how Debbie feels at the beginning of the story?
   - ○ **F.** happy
   - ○ **G.** bored
   - ○ **H.** worried
   - ○ **J.** dreamy

3. Which is a clue that shows how Debbie feels as the plane takes off?
   - ○ **A.** She sits by the window.
   - ○ **B.** She clenches her fists and keeps her eyes closed.
   - ○ **C.** She sits next to her father.
   - ○ **D.** She doesn't get out of her seat.

4. Which clue best shows how Debbie's feelings about flying changed?
   - ○ **F.** She wants to fly to her Grandma's every summer.
   - ○ **G.** She opens her eyes after takeoff.
   - ○ **H.** She looks out the window at the view.
   - ○ **J.** She wants her father to wait for her.

5. Which word best describes how Debbie feels at the end of the story?
   - ○ **A.** worried
   - ○ **B.** bored
   - ○ **C.** upset
   - ○ **D.** relaxed

STOP

Predicting Outcomes

Read the story. Then read each question and fill in the circle next to the best answer.

Sailing for Home

Lee was a quiet man who did things his own way. Rather than working at an office job like many of his friends, Lee became an artist. He also loved to read about other cultures. Yet, later in his life, Lee felt tired and bored, as if he wasn't doing and seeing as much as he could. So, at the age of fifty-seven, Lee bought a boat and set sail for New Zealand from Seattle, Washington.

When he was almost halfway to New Zealand, Lee dropped anchor off the coast of a tiny island in the Pacific Ocean. He swam to shore, and the people there greeted him with warmth, smiles, and a party that lasted all night. Lee hadn't expected this and wasn't prepared for such a warm greeting. He wanted to show respect for the people's customs, so he joined in their fun. He danced and danced even though he was exhausted from the trip.

Four weeks later into his journey, Lee began to run very low on food. He fished for his supper and almost always was successful. Though he went hungry only a few times, he was still very uneasy not knowing when he might catch his next meal.

Lee finally arrived in New Zealand five months after leaving Seattle. Though happy he had made the trip, he felt it would be too difficult to return home by boat. So he placed an ad in a newspaper to try to sell the boat. Meanwhile, he lived on the boat and put fresh paint on it, but it didn't sell. Lee finally bought a plane ticket for home, leaving the boat behind. He had been away from home for almost one year. It was time to go back.

Go on ➡

1. What is Lee likely to do before he goes on another long sailing trip?
    - ○ **A.** learn how to fish
    - ○ **B.** bring enough food
    - ○ **C.** invite a friend along
    - ○ **D.** study the weather maps more closely

2. If Lee decides to visit another unfamiliar place, what is he likely to do before he leaves home?
    - ○ **F.** pack pictures of his home
    - ○ **G.** finish a painting to bring as a gift
    - ○ **H.** buy a gift
    - ○ **J.** study the customs of the people

3. If the islanders had asked Lee to help them finish building a hut, what do you think Lee would have done?
    - ○ **A.** laughed at the idea
    - ○ **B.** swum back to his boat
    - ○ **C.** helped them
    - ○ **D.** asked them for money

4. Which detail is important for predicting Lee's future actions?
    - ○ **F.** He swims to the island.
    - ○ **G.** He fishes for his supper.
    - ○ **H.** He flies back to Seattle.
    - ○ **J.** He respects other people's ways of life.

5. If Lee needed to sell another boat, what might he do differently?
    - ○ **A.** put fresh paint on the boat first
    - ○ **B.** place the ad in more than one place
    - ○ **C.** sail the boat to New Zealand
    - ○ **D.** buy a plane ticket

STOP

Name _____

Text Organization

Read this passage. Then read each question. Fill in the circle next to the best answer.

Sailing Ships of Long Ago

People have been sailing for thousands of years. The boats that were built varied in size and purpose.

Greek Ships

The Greeks built large warships that used a sail and a line of rowers along each side to move the ship. The warships had a large, sharp point on the front. The point was used to ram other boats in battle.

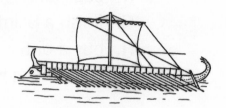

Greek Warship

Roman Ships

The Romans had the largest fleet of working ships in ancient times. They built many huge ships for carrying grain. These ships could carry about a thousand tons of grain and a thousand passengers at once.

Roman Grain Ship

Ships of the Vikings

The Vikings were among the best boat builders of their time. Their strong crafts, called long ships, carried the Vikings across the Atlantic to Greenland and North America. The Vikings were proud of their fine ships.

Viking Long Ship

Go on

1. Which of these is a heading used in the article?
- ○ **A.** Working Ships
- ○ **B.** Greek Warship
- ○ **C.** Roman Ships
- ○ **D.** Sailing Ships of Long Ago

2. Which is a caption for an illustration in the article?
- ○ **F.** Sailing Ships of Long Ago
- ○ **G.** Viking Long Ship
- ○ **H.** Roman Ships
- ○ **J.** Greek Ships

3. Which feature in the article helps the reader understand the difference between the ships?
- ○ **A.** introduction
- ○ **B.** title
- ○ **C.** captions
- ○ **D.** illustrations

4. What is the purpose of the text next to each illustration?
- ○ **F.** to show what the ships looked like
- ○ **G.** to explain the differences among the ships
- ○ **H.** to name the ship
- ○ **J.** to explain how the ships were used

5. Which feature could have been included to help organize the information?
- ○ **A.** a concluding paragraph that describes modern ships
- ○ **B.** more illustrations
- ○ **C.** the dates the ships were in use
- ○ **D.** the name of each boat pictured

STOP

Information and Study Skills

Study the time line below. Then read each question.
Fill in the circle next to the best answer.

Events of Columbus's First Voyage

August 3, 1492 — Columbus's ships, *Niña*, *Pinta*, and *Santa Maria*, leave Spain.

The sailors threaten to turn back.

October 10, 1492

October 12, 1492 — The sailors see land and Columbus goes ashore. He names the island San Salvador.

December 25, 1492 — The *Santa Maria* is wrecked near Haiti.

January 16, 1493 — The *Niña* and *Pinta* begin the journey back to Spain.

February 14, 1493 — The ships become separated during a nighttime storm.

March 15, 1493 — The *Niña* arrives at Palos, Spain. The *Pinta* arrives later the same day.

Go on ⇨

1. In which month did more than one event happen?
   - ○ **A.** August, 1492
   - ○ **B.** October, 1492
   - ○ **C.** January, 1493
   - ○ **D.** February, 1493

2. Which happened before Columbus found San Salvador?
   - ○ **F.** The *Pinta* arrived in Spain.
   - ○ **G.** The *Niña* and *Pinta* became separated during a storm.
   - ○ **H.** The crew threatened to turn back.
   - ○ **J.** The *Niña* and *Pinta* began the journey back to Spain.

3. When was the *Santa Maria* wrecked?
   - ○ **A.** October 12, 1492
   - ○ **B.** December 25, 1492
   - ○ **C.** January 16, 1493
   - ○ **D.** March 15, 1493

4. What happened during February, 1493?
   - ○ **F.** Columbus left Spain.
   - ○ **G.** The sailors saw land.
   - ○ **H.** The *Niña* arrived in Spain.
   - ○ **J.** The *Niña* and the *Pinta* became separated during a storm.

5. How long did it take the *Niña* and *Pinta* to return to Spain?
   - ○ **A.** two months
   - ○ **B.** four months
   - ○ **C.** six months
   - ○ **D.** one year

Name _____

Suffixes

Read each sentence. Then choose the correct base word and ending for each underlined word. Fill in the circle next to the best answer.

1. The divers shone a light through the <u>darkness</u> of the deep ocean.
   - ○ **A.** dare + kness
   - ○ **B.** dark + ness
   - ○ **C.** dar + kness
   - ○ **D.** darkn + ess

2. Long ago, a <u>careless</u> captain had run his ship against the rocks.
   - ○ **F.** car + less
   - ○ **G.** care + less
   - ○ **H.** carele + ss
   - ○ **J.** car + eless

Read each sentence. Then choose the correct word that stands for the underlined words. Fill in the circle next to the best answer.

3. Many thought it was <u>without use</u> to look for the old ship.
   - ○ **A.** useful
   - ○ **B.** used
   - ○ **C.** useless
   - ○ **D.** using

4. One day, the divers' <u>condition of being stubborn</u> finally paid off.
   - ○ **F.** stubbornness
   - ○ **G.** stubbornly
   - ○ **H.** stubbornnless
   - ○ **J.** stubborn

5. They found the ship and its <u>without price</u> treasure.
   - ○ **A.** pricing
   - ○ **B.** priced
   - ○ **C.** priceless
   - ○ **D.** pricey

Name _____

Possessives

Read each sentence. Then find the possessive that correctly replaces the underlined part of the sentence. Fill in the circle next to the best answer.

1. <u>The dream that my dad had</u> was to sail all the way to Mexico.
   - ○ **A.** My dad's dream
   - ○ **B.** The dream's dad
   - ○ **C.** My dads' dream
   - ○ **D.** My dads dream

2. It was <u>an idea my mother had</u> to take the whole family on the trip.
   - ○ **F.** my mothers idea
   - ○ **G.** my mother's idea
   - ○ **H.** my mothers' idea
   - ○ **J.** my moth'ers idea

3. <u>The eyes of my brothers</u> got very big when they heard the plan.
   - ○ **A.** My brothers eye's
   - ○ **B.** My brothers eyes
   - ○ **C.** My brother's eyes
   - ○ **D.** My brothers' eyes

4. <u>The smiles of my sisters</u> made it clear that both girls loved the idea.
   - ○ **F.** My sister's smiles
   - ○ **G.** My sisters' smiles
   - ○ **H.** My sisters smile's
   - ○ **J.** My sisters smiles

5. I couldn't wait for <u>the big adventure of my family</u>.
   - ○ **A.** my familys' big adventure
   - ○ **B.** my families big adventure
   - ○ **C.** my family's big adventure
   - ○ **D.** my families' big adventure

Name _____

VCCV Pattern

Read each sentence. Then find the correct way to divide the underlined word into syllables. Fill in the circle next to the best answer.

1. Teresa and her family were on a very special <u>journey</u>.
   - ○ **A.** journ • ey
   - ○ **B.** jou • rney
   - ○ **C.** jo • ur • ney
   - ○ **D.** jour • ney

2. They were riding on one of the first steam <u>engine</u> trains.
   - ○ **F.** en • gine
   - ○ **G.** e • ngine
   - ○ **H.** engi • ne
   - ○ **J.** eng • ine

3. On the train, they could travel a great <u>distance</u> in one day.
   - ○ **A.** dist • ance
   - ○ **B.** di • stance
   - ○ **C.** dis • tance
   - ○ **D.** distan • ce

4. Teresa smiled as she looked out the <u>window</u> of the train.
   - ○ **F.** wi • ndow
   - ○ **G.** wind • ow
   - ○ **H.** wi • n • dow
   - ○ **J.** win • dow

5. She fell asleep <u>wondering</u> who lived in the homes they passed.
   - ○ **A.** won • dering
   - ○ **B.** won • der • ing
   - ○ **C.** wond • er • ing
   - ○ **D.** wonder • ing

Name _____

Spelling

Read each sentence. Then find the correct way to spell the missing word. Fill in the circle next to your answer.

1. Ms. Dooley traveled across the state in a hot air _____.
   - ○ **A.** balloon
   - ○ **B.** ballune
   - ○ **C.** ballewn
   - ○ **D.** baloon

2. She took her son and her _____ on the trip.
   - ○ **F.** doughter
   - ○ **G.** dawghter
   - ○ **H.** daughter
   - ○ **J.** dawter

3. The Dooleys _____ enough food and water for two days.
   - ○ **A.** braht
   - ○ **B.** brought
   - ○ **C.** brawt
   - ○ **D.** braught

4. They started the trip early _____ morning.
   - ○ **F.** Monnday
   - ○ **G.** Munday
   - ○ **H.** Monday
   - ○ **J.** Mounday

5. They _____ over farms and towns.
   - ○ **A.** floo
   - ○ **B.** flue
   - ○ **C.** floe
   - ○ **D.** flew

6. Things went smoothly until the skies _____ dark and windy.

    ○ **F.** groo   ○ **H.** grew

    ○ **G.** groe   ○ **J.** grue

7. Ms. Dooley had not been expecting the _____ storm.

    ○ **A.** sudden   ○ **C.** sudin

    ○ **B.** suden   ○ **D.** suddin

8. "I think we _____ to land now," she told the children.

    ○ **F.** aught   ○ **H.** oht

    ○ **G.** awht   ○ **J.** ought

9. All three travelers were a little scared _____ they landed safely.

    ○ **A.** untill   ○ **C.** until

    ○ **B.** unntil   ○ **D.** uhntil

10. "That was a trip we'll never _____!" said the children.

    ○ **F.** forghet   ○ **H.** forgett

    ○ **G.** forrget   ○ **J.** forget

STOP

Name _____

Vocabulary

Study the dictionary entries below. Read each question. Fill in the circle next to the best answer.

explorer *noun* Someone who explores an unknown place.
ex•plor•er (ĭk **splôr′**ər) ◆ *noun, plural* **explorers**

sailor *noun* Someone who sails, often as a member of the crew of a ship.
sail•or (sā′ lər) ◆ *noun, plural* **sailors**

1. How many syllables does *sailor* have?

- ○ **A.** one
- ○ **B.** two
- ○ **C.** three
- ○ **D.** four

2. How many syllables does *explorer* have?

- ○ **F.** one
- ○ **G.** two
- ○ **H.** three
- ○ **J.** four

3. Which is the second syllable of *explorer*?

- ○ **A.** ex
- ○ **B.** plo
- ○ **C.** plor
- ○ **D.** er

Read each sentence. Find the word that correctly completes the sentence. Fill in the circle next to your answer.

4. Boat builders used the _____ of many trees to build a big ship.
   - ○ **F.** would
   - ○ **G.** wood
   - ○ **H.** blue
   - ○ **J.** blew

5. The _____ of a ship must be made of strong cloth.
   - ○ **A.** meat
   - ○ **B.** meet
   - ○ **C.** sails
   - ○ **D.** sales

6. Ship is to water as bus is to _____.
   - ○ **F.** land
   - ○ **G.** air
   - ○ **H.** driver
   - ○ **J.** car

7. Track is to train as road is to _____.
   - ○ **A.** home
   - ○ **B.** car
   - ○ **C.** helicopter
   - ○ **D.** street

Go on ⇨

8. <u>Near</u> is to <u>far</u> as <u>small</u> is to _____.

○ **F.** little
○ **G.** size
○ **H.** short
○ **J.** large

9. <u>Suitcase</u> is to <u>traveler</u> as <u>backpack</u> is to _____.

○ **A.** doctor
○ **B.** artist
○ **C.** hiker
○ **D.** sleeping bag

10. <u>Airplane</u> is to <u>pilot</u> as <u>boat</u> is to _____.

○ **F.** captain
○ **G.** ocean
○ **H.** passenger
○ **J.** flyer

Grammar

Read each sentence. Choose the word or phrase that correctly replaces the underlined phrase in each sentence. Fill in the circle next to the answer you choose.

1. <u>My scout troop and I</u> are going to Canada this summer.
    - ○ **A.** Us
    - ○ **B.** We
    - ○ **C.** Me
    - ○ **D.** They

2. We can't wait to see Canada. <u>Canada</u> is a very interesting country.
    - ○ **F.** It
    - ○ **G.** We
    - ○ **H.** He
    - ○ **J.** Him

3. My mother was born in Canada. <u>My mother</u> is glad I will visit there.
    - ○ **A.** He
    - ○ **B.** She
    - ○ **C.** They
    - ○ **D.** Her

4. Some of our parents are going with <u>my troop and me</u>.
    - ○ **F.** it
    - ○ **G.** we
    - ○ **H.** them
    - ○ **J.** us

5. My little sister asked me to send lots of postcards to <u>my little sister</u>.
    - ○ **A.** us
    - ○ **B.** him
    - ○ **C.** her
    - ○ **D.** she

Go on ⇨

6. We have been writing to Canadian pen pals and will get to meet <u>our pen pals</u>.

    ○ **F.** us   ○ **H.** them

    ○ **G.** him   ○ **J.** you

7. Mr. Fox will drive the van, and Mr. Costa will help <u>Mr. Fox</u>.

    ○ **A.** him   ○ **C.** them

    ○ **B.** he   ○ **D.** you

8. I am going to keep a diary of <u>the places that are favorites to me</u>.

    ○ **F.** their favorite places

    ○ **G.** my favorite places

    ○ **H.** his favorite places

    ○ **J.** we favorite places

9. We are taking <u>the camping gear that belongs to us</u> so we can stay at campgrounds.

    ○ **A.** us camping gear

    ○ **B.** their camping gear

    ○ **C.** my camping gear

    ○ **D.** our camping gear

10. Did you ever go on a long trip with <u>the friends you have</u>?

    ○ **F.** your friends

    ○ **G.** her friends

    ○ **H.** our friends

    ○ **J.** their friends

Name _____

Writing Skills

Read each group of sentences. Choose the correct date or time that replaces the underlined words. Fill in the circle next to the answer you choose.

1. The <u>fourteenth of June in 2000</u> was one of my favorite days.
   - ○ **A.** June, 14, 2000
   - ○ **B.** June 14 2000
   - ○ **C.** June, 14 2000
   - ○ **D.** June 14, 2000

2. We left New York at <u>seven thirty in the morning</u>.
   - ○ **F.** 7:30 A.M
   - ○ **G.** 7:30 AM
   - ○ **H.** 7:30 A.M.
   - ○ **J.** 730 AM.

3. Our plane landed in Berlin, Germany, at <u>six forty-five in the evening</u>.
   - ○ **A.** 6:45 P.M.
   - ○ **B.** 6:45 PM
   - ○ **C.** 6:45 PM.
   - ○ **D.** 645 P.M.

4. When we got to Germany it was <u>eleven o'clock at night</u>.
   - ○ **F.** 1100 P.M.
   - ○ **G.** 11:00 P.M.
   - ○ **H.** 11,00 PM
   - ○ **J.** 11:00 P:M

5. We stayed in Germany until the <u>second of July in 2000</u>.
   - ○ **A.** July 2/2000
   - ○ **B.** July, 2 2000
   - ○ **C.** July/2/2000
   - ○ **D.** July 2, 2000

Smart Solutions

Level 3, Theme 6

Theme Skills Test Record

Student _____ Date _____

Student Record Form

	Possible Score	Criterion Score	Student Score
Part A: Problem Solving and Decision Making	5	4	
Part B: Drawing Conclusions	5	4	
Part C: Making Generalizations	5	4	
Part D: Information and Study Skills	5	4	
Part E: VCCCV Pattern	5	4	
Part F: VCV Pattern	5	4	
Part G: Contractions	5	4	
Part H: Spelling	10	8	
Part I: Vocabulary	10	8	
Part J: Grammar	10	8	
Part K: Writing Skills	5.	4	
TOTAL	70	56	
Total Student Score x 1.43 =			%

Name _____

Problem Solving and Decision Making

Read this story. Then read each question. Fill in the circle next to the best answer.

A New Friend

Charlotte had been in her new school for over a month and had not made any friends.

"Charlotte," said Ms. Taylor, "if you would talk to the other students, they'd be your friends." But when other students invited her to join their work group, Charlotte just shook her head and worked by herself. She wanted to make friends, but she was simply too shy.

One day there was another new student in the class. His name was Ed. The new boy sat at the empty desk next to Charlotte. When the teacher introduced Ed to the class, she used sign language while she spoke. Ed watched carefully. When Ms. Taylor told Ed that she was happy to have him in the class, he made the sign for *thank you*. He put one hand flat against his mouth then moved it away and placed it flat against his other hand. His lips said "Thank you," but he did not make a sound.

When Ed sat down, he waved at Charlotte and his lips said "Hi." Charlotte waved back shyly. Ed took a book out of his pack and handed it to Charlotte. The book showed the hand signs for words and letters. Charlotte smiled and made the same sign for *thank you* that Ed had made earlier. She wrote a note and passed it to Ed.

Ed read the note and grinned. He moved his lips and signed, "Yes, you can be my friend. Can I be yours?"

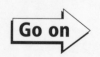

1. What problem does Charlotte have?
   - ○ **A.** The other students are mean to her.
   - ○ **B.** Her teacher does not notice her.
   - ○ **C.** She is too shy to make friends.
   - ○ **D.** She doesn't like the other students.

2. How is her problem solved?
   - ○ **F.** She writes a note to Ed, asking to be his friend.
   - ○ **G.** Her classmates ask her to join in the work group.
   - ○ **H.** She waves hello to Ed.
   - ○ **J.** Ed sits next to Charlotte.

3. What is a reason to think that Charlotte's solution is a good one?
   - ○ **A.** She will now feel comfortable talking to the other students.
   - ○ **B.** Charlotte can now join others in group work.
   - ○ **C.** Charlotte can feel comfortable with the other students.
   - ○ **D.** She and Ed are both new students who can help each other.

4. What is a reason to think that Charlotte's decision is a poor one?
   - ○ **F.** She has to learn sign language.
   - ○ **G.** She still doesn't have to talk.
   - ○ **H.** She'll be called on more often in class.
   - ○ **J.** She'll still be alone.

5. What other way could Charlotte have successfully solved her problem?
   - ○ **A.** written down everything she wanted to say
   - ○ **B.** sent a letter to her teacher
   - ○ **C.** joined one of the children's work groups
   - ○ **D.** asked her father to let her stay at home

STOP

Name _____

Drawing Conclusions

Read this passage. Then read each question. Fill in the circle next to the best answer.

A Close Call

Scott smiled as he headed downstairs. It was his mother's special day, and he had hidden her gift in a box behind some bags in the basement. Scott had saved his allowance for six weeks. Then he had gone to his mother's favorite department store and asked the clerk to help him pick out a necklace. He even paid to have the necklace gift-wrapped. He couldn't wait to see his mother's face when she opened the beautiful present.

Scott went to the corner where the gift was hidden. But where were all the bags of old clothes? Scott looked all around. He was very worried and upset.

"Mom!" he called up the stairs. "Where are the bags of clothes that were down here?"

"Oh, that old junk? I had your father take them to the thrift store," she answered. "There are some rags in the laundry room if you're cleaning your bike."

Scott ran to the garage and hopped on his bike. He rode as fast as he could toward the thrift store. He was only halfway there when he saw his father driving toward home. It was too late. Scott felt like crying.

Scott's father pulled over and called, "Hey, Scott! Do you know anything about this?" He held up a long, thin, velvet box.

Scott grinned with relief. "I sure do, Dad. I sure do."

1. On what day does this story most likely take place?
   - ○ **A.** Mother's Day
   - ○ **B.** Fourth of July
   - ○ **C.** Thanksgiving
   - ○ **D.** Valentine's Day

2. What detail leads you to conclude what day it is?
   - ○ **F.** Scott bought a necklace.
   - ○ **G.** It was his mother's special day.
   - ○ **H.** Scott's father had the box.
   - ○ **J.** Scott was worried when he couldn't find the box.

3. Why does Scott feel like crying when he sees his father driving home?
   - ○ **A.** Scott was lost.
   - ○ **B.** He was relieved that he found his father.
   - ○ **C.** He thought the necklace had been given away.
   - ○ **D.** His dad didn't stop.

4. Why does Scott smile when his father shows him the box?
   - ○ **F.** He realizes the necklace is safe.
   - ○ **G.** Scott thinks the box has a gift for him in it.
   - ○ **H.** It's his father's gift to his mother.
   - ○ **J.** It's a pretty box.

5. What detail about the box supports your conclusion about why Scott grins?
   - ○ **A.** It's made of velvet.
   - ○ **B.** It's long and thin like a necklace.
   - ○ **C.** It's the size that a watch could fit in.
   - ○ **D.** It looks like it holds jewelry that his father might have bought.

STOP

Making Generalizations

Read this passage. Then read each question. Fill in the circle next to the best answer.

Too Many Sisters

Terry stomped out of the room she shared with her three younger sisters and yelled, "Who took my purple hair band and my flowered T-shirt? Lisa? Emily? You're always taking my things!"

In the one bathroom the children shared, she found her glitter-pink nail polish spilled on her favorite magazine. The magazine was even ripped and crumpled. As usual, wet towels were in a pile on the floor. "Sarah! Sarah, where are you?" No one answered. "Why can't they leave me alone?" she complained to herself.

Terry stormed back into the bedroom and found one of her two brothers sitting on her bed. "What are you doing, Bryan? Did someone say you could come in here?" He silently shook his head. Terry sighed heavily but didn't say anything else to Bryan. She knew he would miss her.

Terry hurriedly looked around for her sleeping bag but couldn't find it among the clothes, toys, and books that littered the floor. "I need my own room. I can never find anything in here!" Terry thought to herself.

Terry grabbed her things and hurried downstairs with Bryan running behind. When she opened the front door, she stared in amazement. There stood her sisters and brothers holding a banner that said *World's Best Big Sister! We'll miss you. Have fun at camp!* Lisa was wearing the purple hair band. Emily was wearing the flowered T-shirt. Sarah's nails were glittery pink.

They all waved and shouted good-bye as the car pulled away.

1. What generalization does Terry make about her sisters?
   - ○ **A.** They take her flowered shirts.
   - ○ **B.** They are always taking her things.
   - ○ **C.** They take her hair bands.
   - ○ **D.** They all share one bathroom.

2. Which detail supports the generalization that Terry's little sisters always make a mess?
   - ○ **F.** Bryan is sitting on Terry's bed.
   - ○ **G.** Terry asks why she can't be left alone.
   - ○ **H.** Sarah doesn't answer when Terry calls for her.
   - ○ **J.** Wet towels are left on the bathroom floor.

3. Which detail supports the generalization that Terry can never find anything in her room?
   - ○ **A.** Terry sighs when Bryan shakes his head.
   - ○ **B.** Terry complains that she needs her own room.
   - ○ **C.** Terry can't find her sleeping bag.
   - ○ **D.** All the sisters share one room.

4. Which detail supports the generalization that younger brothers and sisters look up to their older brothers and sisters?
   - ○ **F.** Bryan runs down the stairs behind Terry.
   - ○ **G.** Terry's sisters are wearing her clothes.
   - ○ **H.** The sign reads *World's Best Big Sister!*
   - ○ **J.** Everyone waved as Terry left.

5. What generalization can you make about Terry's sisters wearing her things at the end of the story?
   - ○ **A.** It is a way of showing that they will miss her.
   - ○ **B.** Sisters always take things from each other.
   - ○ **C.** They can't wait for her to leave.
   - ○ **D.** They don't have things of their own.

STOP

Name _____

Information and Study Skills

Read this passage. Then read each question. Fill in the circle next to the best answer.

Smart Saver Piggy Bank

Do you spend your allowance the moment you get it? Try making this piggy bank and filling it up. You'll be surprised by what you can buy with your savings!

Collect the following items before you start. You'll need a two-liter plastic soda bottle with a cap screwed on, tape, three small cardboard tubes, many strips of newspaper, and a pair of scissors. Also, get two cups of flour, two cups of water, and a large bowl from the kitchen. Lastly, you'll need a pipe cleaner, some craft paint, and paint brushes.

To begin, cut two of the cardboard tubes in half to make the legs. Cut triangles out of the other tube for the ears. Attach all of these pieces to the bottle with tape. Next, stick the pipe cleaner into the end of the bottle. Curl the pipe cleaner so it looks like a pig's tail. Next, mix the flour and water in the large bowl until they form a smooth paste. After you've made the paste, dip the newspaper strips into it. Place the newspaper strips over the soda bottle, the legs, the ears, and the tail.

Leave the pig to dry overnight. The next day, paint your piggy bank with your favorite colors. Finally, ask an adult for help cutting the slot where you will put your money.

Congratulations, you've made a piggy bank! Whenever you have change in your pockets, you can put it in your bank. When the pig is full, you can buy yourself something special!

1. Which is something you need for making the piggy bank?
   - ○ **A.** buttons
   - ○ **B.** paper plates
   - ○ **C.** felt
   - ○ **D.** a soda bottle

2. Why should you cut and attach the legs **before** you paste on the newspaper strips?
   - ○ **F.** so the pieces will not get lost
   - ○ **G.** so the paint will dry faster
   - ○ **H.** so the newspaper will cover over the tubes
   - ○ **J.** so the slot can be cut into the bottle more easily

3. What is the next step **after** placing the newspaper strips on the pig's body?
   - ○ **A.** Leave the bottle to dry overnight.
   - ○ **B.** Paint it.
   - ○ **C.** Mix the flour and water into a paste.
   - ○ **D.** Collect the rest of the materials.

4. At what point should you ask for an adult's help?
   - ○ **F.** when gathering materials
   - ○ **G.** when cutting the slot for the money
   - ○ **H.** when mixing the paste
   - ○ **J.** when covering the pig in newspaper strips

5. How long will it take to make this piggy bank?
   - ○ **A.** about an hour
   - ○ **B.** half a day
   - ○ **C.** two hours
   - ○ **D.** more than one day

STOP

Name _____

VCCCV Pattern

Read each sentence. Then choose the best way to divide each underlined word into syllables. Fill in the circle next to your answer.

1. Sometimes my baby brother Sammy gets out of <u>control</u>.
   - ○ **A.** contr • ol
   - ○ **B.** cont • rol
   - ○ **C.** con • tr • ol
   - ○ **D.** con • trol

2. He tried to <u>improve</u> the model of the solar system I made.
   - ○ **F.** imp • rove
   - ○ **G.** i • mpr • ove
   - ○ **H.** im • prove
   - ○ **J.** imp • ro • ve

3. Sammy looked like a huge <u>monster</u> tearing apart the planets.
   - ○ **A.** mon • ster
   - ○ **B.** mons • ter
   - ○ **C.** mon • st • er
   - ○ **D.** monst • er

4. <u>Instead</u> of getting mad, I just had to laugh.
   - ○ **F.** Ins • tead
   - ○ **G.** In • ste • ad
   - ○ **H.** Inst • ead
   - ○ **J.** In • stead

5. I can never stay <u>angry</u> at him because he's too young to know better.
   - ○ **A.** a • ngr • y
   - ○ **B.** an • gry
   - ○ **C.** angr • y
   - ○ **D.** an • gr • y

Name _____

VCV Pattern

Read each sentence. Then choose the best way to divide each underlined word into syllables. Fill in the circle next to your answer.

1. My dad almost missed our <u>vacation</u>.
   - ○ **A.** va • ca • tion
   - ○ **B.** vac • at • ion
   - ○ **C.** vaca • tion
   - ○ **D.** va • cation

2. Something was wrong with the <u>motor</u> of his car.
   - ○ **F.** mot • or
   - ○ **G.** mo • tor
   - ○ **H.** mo • t • or
   - ○ **J.** mo • to • r

3. We were to meet at the airport and <u>travel</u> to Florida.
   - ○ **A.** trav • el
   - ○ **B.** tra • vel
   - ○ **C.** trave • l
   - ○ **D.** tra • ve • l

4. When the <u>pilot</u> arrived, we knew it would soon be time to take off.
   - ○ **F.** pil • ot
   - ○ **G.** p • il • ot
   - ○ **H.** pilo • t
   - ○ **J.** pi • lot

5. At the last minute, Dad jumped out of a <u>taxi</u> and rushed to meet us.
   - ○ **A.** ta • xi
   - ○ **B.** ta • x • i
   - ○ **C.** tax • i
   - ○ **D.** t • axi

G Name _____

Contractions

Read each sentence. Choose the words that stand for the underlined word. Fill in the circle next to the best answer.

1. <u>I'm</u> not very good at soccer, but I love going to the games.
   - ○ **A.** I would
   - ○ **B.** It is
   - ○ **C.** I can
   - ○ **D.** I am

2. My best friend says <u>he's</u> going to be captain of the team.
   - ○ **F.** he did
   - ○ **G.** he is
   - ○ **H.** he would
   - ○ **J.** he will

3. My sisters think <u>they'll</u> both make the soccer team.
   - ○ **A.** they would
   - ○ **B.** they will
   - ○ **C.** they were
   - ○ **D.** there will

4. I <u>don't</u> want to miss out on all the fun.
   - ○ **F.** do not
   - ○ **G.** did not
   - ○ **H.** will not
   - ○ **J.** does not

5. The coach said <u>he'd</u> let me be the equipment manager!
   - ○ **A.** he did
   - ○ **B.** he is
   - ○ **C.** he would
   - ○ **D.** he will

Name _____

Spelling

**Read each sentence. Then find the correct way to spell
the missing word. Fill in the circle next to your answer.**

1. Mom says I can't go to Camp Arrowhead _____ I would miss the
   family trip.
   - ○ **A.** because
   - ○ **B.** becaus
   - ○ **C.** bacause
   - ○ **D.** becuz

2. Every _____ I have the same problem.
   - ○ **F.** summir
   - ○ **G.** sumer
   - ○ **H.** summer
   - ○ **J.** summar

3. My best friend Max goes to camp, but I am not _____ to go.
   - ○ **A.** abel
   - ○ **B.** able
   - ○ **C.** abele
   - ○ **D.** abell

4. I like family trips, but I don't like it when Max is not _____.
   - ○ **F.** ahround
   - ○ **G.** arownd
   - ○ **H.** uround
   - ○ **J.** around

5. Max promised me a surprise _____ he left this summer.
   - ○ **A.** befor
   - ○ **B.** before
   - ○ **C.** behfore
   - ○ **D.** bifore

6. "I bet you _____ mind getting something in the mail," he said.

- ○ **F.** would'nt
- ○ **G.** wouldn't
- ○ **H.** woodn't
- ○ **J.** woudn't

7. "I guess so," I said. "But _____ rather go to Camp Arrowhead with you!"

- ○ **A.** Id'
- ○ **B.** I'de
- ○ **C.** Id'e
- ○ **D.** I'd

8. Just then, I didn't think I would _____ get to go to Camp Arrowhead.

- ○ **F.** evir
- ○ **G.** evver
- ○ **H.** ever
- ○ **J.** evre

9. "Look, _____ been sent a video!" said my mom, a month later.

- ○ **A.** you've
- ○ **B.** youve
- ○ **C.** youv'e
- ○ **D.** yoo've

10. It was Max on the video. "I _____ bring you to camp, so I'm bringing Camp Arrowhead to you!"

- ○ **F.** cudn't
- ○ **G.** could'nt
- ○ **H.** couldn't
- ○ **J.** couldnt

STOP

Name _____

Vocabulary

Read each sentence. Then choose the word that means the opposite of the underlined word. Fill in the circle next to the best answer.

1. Nancy was going to take a <u>difficult</u> test.
    - ○ **A.** hard
    - ○ **B.** long
    - ○ **C.** written
    - ○ **D.** easy

2. All week, her sister helped her study until <u>sunset</u>.
    - ○ **F.** nighttime
    - ○ **G.** sunrise
    - ○ **H.** evening
    - ○ **J.** morning

3. After all her studying, Nancy felt <u>prepared</u> for the test.
    - ○ **A.** hopeful
    - ○ **B.** ready
    - ○ **C.** unready
    - ○ **D.** nervous

Read each sentence. Then choose the word that means the same or nearly the same as the underlined word. Fill in the circle next to the best answer.

4. The next morning, however, Nancy felt <u>unsure</u> that she would do well.
    - ○ **F.** certain
    - ○ **G.** confident
    - ○ **H.** weak
    - ○ **J.** doubtful

5. During the test, all the students worked <u>silently</u>.

  ○ **A.** noisily   ○ **C.** hard

  ○ **B.** quietly   ○ **D.** thoughtfully

6. Nancy was <u>thrilled</u> when she received a high grade on her test.

  ○ **F.** delighted   ○ **H.** quiet

  ○ **G.** ashamed   ○ **J.** puzzled

Study the spelling table below. Use the table to find the answer to each question. Fill in the circle next to the best answer.

Sound	Spellings	Sample Words
/ă/	a, au	bat, have, la**u**gh
/ā/	a, ai	made, later, r**ai**n
	ay, ea	pl**ay**, gr**ea**t
/â/	air, ar, are	f**air**, sc**ar**ce, c**are**
	eir, ere	th**eir**, wh**ere**
/ä/	a, al	f**a**ther, c**al**m

7. What vowel sound is in the sample word *laugh*?

  ○ **A.** /ă/

  ○ **B.** /ā/

  ○ **C.** /ä/

  ○ **D.** /â/

8. Which word has the same vowel spelling as the sample word *play*?

- ○ **F.** subway
- ○ **G.** pattern
- ○ **H.** shook
- ○ **J.** under

9. Which sample word has the same vowel sound as the word *cable*?

- ○ **A.** rain
- ○ **B.** fair
- ○ **C.** calm
- ○ **D.** laugh

10. What are two spellings of the vowel sound you hear in the sample word *father*?

- ○ **F.** ay, ea
- ○ **G.** air, ar
- ○ **H.** a, al
- ○ **J.** eir, ere

J Name _____

Grammar

Read each sentence. Find the word that correctly completes the sentence. Fill in the circle next to your answer.

1. Allen's class was going on _____ field trip to a farm.
   ○ **A.** a   ○ **C.** tasty
   ○ **B.** an   ○ **D.** few

2. He made sure that he packed _____ oranges on the kitchen counter.
   ○ **F.** a   ○ **H.** the
   ○ **G.** an   ○ **J.** few

3. Allen found _____ open seat next to Jack on the bus.
   ○ **A.** an   ○ **C.** some
   ○ **B.** a   ○ **D.** two

4. It took a _____ time to reach the farm.
   ○ **F.** long   ○ **H.** happy
   ○ **G.** one   ○ **J.** the

5. Allen couldn't wait to eat his _____ oranges.
   ○ **A.** one   ○ **C.** the
   ○ **B.** two   ○ **D.** easy

6. When it was lunchtime, Allen realized he had the _____ lunch in the class.

    ○ **F.** too small   ○ **H.** smaller

    ○ **G.** small   ○ **J.** smallest

7. The teacher said, "Eat _____, please. We're leaving in ten minutes."

    ○ **A.** faster   ○ **C.** never

    ○ **B.** loudly   ○ **D.** secretly

8. Jack _____ tapped Allen's shoulder.

    ○ **F.** gentle   ○ **H.** gentler

    ○ **G.** gently   ○ **J.** gentlest

9. Allen turned _____. "Would you like my orange?" asked Jack.

    ○ **A.** today   ○ **C.** around

    ○ **B.** slow   ○ **D.** often

10. Allen laughed. "Thanks, Jack, can I have it _____?

    ○ **F.** later   ○ **H.** late

    ○ **G.** lately   ○ **J.** lateness

Name _____

Writing Skills

Read each sentence. Then choose the sentence that has an adverb which tells how or when. Fill in the circle next to the best answer.

1. ○ **A.** Katy woke up and stretched.
    ○ **B.** Katy woke up early.
    ○ **C.** Katy couldn't wake up.
    ○ **D.** Katy woke up and smiled.

2. ○ **F.** She thought about her friend's slumber party.
    ○ **G.** She thought about her best friend's party.
    ○ **H.** She thought about her friend's big party.
    ○ **J.** She thought excitedly about her friend's party.

3. ○ **A.** Katy quickly planned ways to earn money for a gift.
    ○ **B.** Katy planned ways to earn money for a birthday gift.
    ○ **C.** Katy planned ways to earn money for an expensive gift.
    ○ **D.** Katy planned ways to earn spending money for a gift.

4. ○ **F.** She weeded the garden and washed the car.
   ○ **G.** She weeded the garden and washed the new car.
   ○ **H.** She soon weeded the garden and washed the car.
   ○ **J.** She weeded the rose garden and washed the car.

5. ○ **A.** When her mother paid her, Katy headed to the music store.
   ○ **B.** When her mother paid her, Katy eagerly headed to the store.
   ○ **C.** When her mother and father paid her, Katy headed to the store.
   ○ **D.** When her mother paid her, Katy headed to the store on her bike.

STOP